Practical Robotics and Interfacing for the Spectrum

Other books on the Spectrum

An Expert Guide to the Spectrum
Mike James
0 246 12278 1

Introducing Spectrum Machine Code
Ian Sinclair
0 246 12082 7

40 Educational Games for the Spectrum
Vince Apps
0 246 12233 1

Make the Most of Your ZX Microdrive
Ian Sinclair
0 246 12406 7

The Spectrum Book of Games
Mike James, S. M. Gee, and Kay Ewbank
0 246 12047 9

Spectrum Gamesmaster
Kay Ewbank, Mike James, and S. M. Gee
0 246 12515 2

Spectrum Graphics and Sound
Steve Money
0 246 12192 0

The Spectrum Programmer
S. M. Gee
0 246 12025 8

The ZX Spectrum and How to Get the Most from It
Ian Sinclair
0 246 12018 5

Practical Robotics and Interfacing for the Spectrum

A. A. Berk

GRANADA
London Toronto Sydney New York

Granada Technical Books
Granada Publishing Ltd
8 Grafton Street, London W1X 3LA

First published in Great Britain by
Granada Publishing 1984

Distributed in the United States of America
by Sheridan House, Inc.

British Library Cataloguing in Publication Data
Berk, A.A.
Practical robotics and interfacing with the Spectrum.
1. Robots   2. Sinclair ZX Spectrum (Computer)
I. Title
629.8'92   TJ211

ISBN 0-246-12576-4

Typeset by V & M Graphics Ltd, Aylesbury, Bucks
Printed and bound in Great Britain by
Mackays of Chatham, Kent

Contents

Preface

Robotics is probably the most emotive of all the computer-related subjects. It is also one of the most badly defined. A robot, to the non-technical person, is a human-like machine (an android), perhaps indistinguishable from the real thing, and probably on the verge of taking over our world and kicking us all out of work. To the engineer, however, the word 'robot' has a simpler and wider meaning, and would broadly include any machine capable of automatic control of a situation. Engineers disagree on the actual definition, but most would agree that the device should have some sort of 'feedback' control within it, which is a type of intelligence. Other engineers would insist on some type of 'learning' response in the device. No engineer would insist on anything resembling a human, for one very good reason – engineers are practical people, and they know this is impossible at present! However, it should be mentioned here that it is the secret dream of everyone in the field to copy, with improvements, all the human faculties.

This book aims to give an overall view of the simple electronic techniques which might be employed by any practical person with a few hours to spare, and a Spectrum which he or she has learned to program in BASIC. The eventual result will not be an android, with a Spectrum for a heart, but a set of straightforward circuit ideas, and useful pieces of information to allow the reader to explore fully the fascinating area of robotics.

The book starts with an introduction to robotics, followed by an explanation of the Spectrum's electronics. This builds upon knowledge which any Spectrum owner already has about the machine. The next chapter gives an example of a simple control application using the Spectrum. Chapter 3 describes a special interface for controlling robots. This is used to control a simple light-seeking robot mouse. Chapter 4 explains the fundamentals of controlling stepper motors, shows you how to use a speech synthesiser, and explains how to monitor parameters which vary continuously, such as the ambient light level. Chapter 5 reviews some of the lowest cost robot arms on the market, and describes one in particular as an add-on to the Spectrum. Appendices describe binary numbers and electronics, and introduce the complete beginner to ideas which are needed for an understanding of the book.

Only BASIC is used, but those familiar with machine code will be able to transfer the ideas accordingly. Also, the projects described do not tie up the Spectrum full-time – the machine is still available for all its ordinary uses. The book carefully explains how everything works, and makes it possible for you to design and build your own peripherals as you think of the projects for yourself.

Finally, there are several people who have given me assistance in the preparation of the material for this book, and I should like to mention two in particular. My sincerest thanks are due to my wife for her encouragement and support, and for drawing up the figures to make them comprehensible to the publisher's draughtsmen. Similar thanks are due to my father, for his considerable help with the general and technical proof reading.

A. A. Berk

Chapter One
Introduction to Robotics and the Spectrum's Electronics

What is robotics?

The science fiction writer Isaac Asimov has probably been the single most powerful influence on our conception of *Robotics*. His stories tell of a world where humanoids are manufactured with all the intelligent faculties of humans, and few of their mechanical failings. The complexity of the minute control of these machines is relegated to a 'positronic brain', a block of material within which are formed millions upon millions of data pathways, very similar to the biological paths within the human brain. These positronic brains are many times more efficient than ours in such activities as total recall and mental calculation. They never wear out, and require little energy to keep them going.

In addition to the miracle of this control mechanism, Asimov's robots have all the motor characteristics of humans, but with considerably greater strength and general physical efficiency. They also have the advantage that faulty parts are easily replaced. Asimov's robots look like humans, and they communicate in normal speech.

The picture is one of an ideal robot – at present rather wishful thinking. However, the influence of these ideas makes us all imagine a future where the drudgery of everyday life can be assigned to machines, leaving us free to enjoy the fruits of their labour.

Regrettably, many more inventions – as revolutionary as the invention of the transistor itself – are required before this ideal state can be achieved. Even so, present day robotics is influenced by the desire to re-create human faculties in machines – simply because such machines need to be able to communicate with humans and take instructions from them. It is often argued that this is best achieved by their being as close to human form as possible, to minimise barriers in the *man-machine interface*.

The above reasoning has led to research in a number of specific areas. The ones whose products will be used in this book are, broadly speaking, the control of arm-like movements, speech synthesis, and general locomotion. Vision is one of the most difficult, but work is proceding on TV camera-based intelligent vision units, and light detectors are already developed to a fine art. Various classes of sensor are also possible, such as touch, using microswitches, and temperature and pressure using electronic devices.

Reproducing human characteristics by machine is a very time-consuming and detailed process. This is particularly so as we are still learning about the human animal. However, we are already making devices which are more efficient in some sense. For instance, we can now produce near-perfect human speech. Each word is stored in a memory, and may be called up by a specific electronic label, as we shall see in Chapter 4. Automatically, we have produced a system that has total recall, something humans cannot achieve. Theoretically, every word could also be varied in pitch and tone of copy the speech of different types of individuals. Hence, a complete theatre production could be produced, with as many voices as you wish, male and female, from this one data bank of words, simply by varying a few electronic parameters.

Electronic systems can be designed to work for very long periods with few failures. Any failures are remedied by simply replacing defective parts. No human can be so reliable, or repaired so easily! A simple bout of 'flu, for instance, can put a human being out of operation for days or weeks.

The science of robotics, based on machinery and electronics, gives us the ability in theory to endow the final product with all the characteristics we wish *we* had. Of course, the most important of these is that of general intelligence. This is so complex a concept that only the most superficial description exists. Many people would include such qualities as the ability to learn, make decisions, solve problems, and so on. These are all abstract ideas which computer scientists are constantly investigating. This book is concerned with the more mechanical aspects of robotics, and the next sections describe some human characteristics which are at least partially reproducible.

Vision

The eye is a remarkable object, and is still only partly understood. The way in which we see depends upon light from objects in our surroundings passing into the eyeball, and being focussed onto the retina at the back of the eye. This retina is like a projection screen, but contains a biochemically complex structure which converts the image into nerve impulses for processing by the brain. However, the eye itself also performs some of the processing of this data, rather than simply converting light impulses into nerve impulses and leaving it to the brain to sort it all out. For instance, the eye is good at detecting movement. This characteristic is particularly active in the outside edge of the retina, and has led to a figure of speech – 'out of the corner of your eye'. You will find that even though you cannot see clearly at the edge of your vision, if something moves in that part of the field, your eyes are immediately attracted to it.

Other processing includes a certain amount of recognition of patterns. Again, this aspect of vision has passed into language with expressions such as 'getting your eye in' for certain activities. This literally means training the vision system to recognise certain specific aspects of the visual field in an unconscious manner. Simple types of processing can now be performed on a visual field viewed by a TV camera. The straightforward sensing of light and dark has been possible for some time, and a project is described in Chapter 3 which uses light sensing for controlling a robot mouse.

We are many years from even the most fundamental type of human intelligence in vision. Simple things are very complex to reproduce, e.g. recognising a particular human being, or being able to teach a machine what a table looks like and rely upon it to recognise a table of any type, in any setting. However, the things we can do are an important start, and anyone can experiment with these ideas, and perhaps even push the boundaries a little further forward. Most of these fields are only in their infancy, and the potential for discovery is enormous.

Hearing

The detection and storage of sounds, even their analysis into different frequencies, is well understood. We can detect sound to very low levels indeed, as well as over frequency ranges far in excess of that of the human ear. Microphone technology is able to provide conversion into electronic waveforms so accurately, and electronics reproduce to such a fine degree, that it is often impossible to distinguish reproduced from real sound in the correct environment. In addition, the brain is able to tell from which direction a sound is coming by the difference in time taken by the sound to reach each ear. This can be emulated by electronics to a considerably finer degree than in the human ear, and is part of the study of radar and underwater sonics.

These aspects, however, are the straightforward side to hearing. Human hearing is rather more than a simple sound detection unit. It is capable of distinguishing patterns in the sound, matching them up with experience and viewing them intelligently. This is, again, a form of pattern recognition. The intelligence of the acoustic system is bound up with communication, and general intelligence. For instance, how would one teach a machine to appreciate music? To answer questions such as this, we must look inside ourselves, where the study of psychology comes in useful. The art of reproducing human qualities can only come from a deep understanding of our own nature.

Touch

There are several levels to the sense of touch. The first level is simply the ability to sense the presence of an object. This can be achieved electronically by a number of sensors, to almost any degree of positional accuracy.

The second level of touch is to be able to distinguish between different types of object or surface composition. This is also possible electronically in a variety of ways, and machines can be made to work in environments and places where humans would be injured. This level also includes sensing of temperature, pressure, movement, etc. The science of sensors for physical phenomena is quite advanced, and one should be able to find or make a sensor for most uses.

The third level concerns the ability to detect patterns, and relate them to previous experience. This is more than simply measuring the size of a square, say, or the area of a disk, which machinery can be made to do. It is very similar to pattern recognition in vision, whereby a human can recognise a table, for example. Humans are not particularly good at pattern recognition by touch, but they are many times better than any machine we can yet build. Solving the problems of intelligent pattern recognition in vision may well solve the problems of this level of touch too.

Speech

There are two aspects to human speech – *synthesis* and *recognition*. Again, there is a pattern recognition element to the second of these.

Speech synthesis is well understood today, though this is only the most superficial level of speech. Humans use speech for communication, and a large part of the brain is devoted to this function. It is very complex, and as remarkable as vision. It will be some time before machines can properly recognise words spoken by any (as opposed to a single) individual and communicate back in an intelligent manner.

There are many types of speech synthesis system on the market at present, and these may be split into a number of classes. Two classes of importance are *stored speech*, and *synthesis by rule*. The first takes in a complete human word, through a microphone, analyses the voltage variations produced, and stores the data in as compact a form as possible. That word may then be 'played back' using a special electronic circuit by feeding it the stored data. This type of system is cheap to buy, and manufacturers have a large store of standard words from which they can draw for any given application.

Synthesis by rule is a more intelligent method of producing speech, and considerably more versatile. It normally takes the form of a device which can be fed human words, separated into letters, using the ASCII code, with each pair of words separated by a space. The synthesiser then tries to put together the sounds for that word by using a set of rules, and building the word-sound up from a basic set of approximately fifty standard sounds called *phonemes* or *allophones*, from which any word can be made. Theoretically, it will use the same rules as we learn when we are children, and hence would be able to say any word given to it. For instance, given the word 'hello', it would first recognise an 'H' sound. Then the 'E' would be pronounced as in 'red', the way most single 'E's are pronounced – this is an example of a rule. The 'L' sound comes next, and can only be pronounced one way. The 'O' on the end could be pronounced in several ways. However, it would probably decide that 'O' on the end of a word would more commonly be pronounced as in 'rode'. These sounds make up the familiar word 'hello'. The problem, of course, is that human languages are full of special cases, which have evolved in our very human manner of producing great depth and sophistication without perfect organisation.

In order to circumvent this problem, most working synthesisers have a large store of special cases for words. Thus, when a word is presented for speaking, the synthesiser tries to match it up with a standard word in its memory, for which it already has the rules and phonemes worked out.

This provides an excellent example, of course, of a learning response. Synthesisers can easily be built to update the memory in some manner when given a new word. A typical process might be as follows. The word is presented. If it is spoken wrongly, the synthesiser is changed over to 'learn' mode. The word is then presented in a special phonetic spelling which gives the phonemes. The machine is told the correct spelling, and stores the phonetic data against the spelling in its memory. Unfortunately there are some problems. First, memory space, and secondly the time required for retrieval. Memory which can be altered, and then not lost when power is removed from the system, is bulky and expensive. The second problem is even more serious. It could take some time to sort through a very large file of words for the one required, depending upon the type of memory chosen. If not found, the word still has to be synthesised by rule, and this takes yet more time.

The problems above are on the verge of being solved, however, and synthesis by rule is sure to be the real future of speech synthesis. At present, such devices do not give speech to the same near-perfection as stored speech systems; they normally sound 'liquid' and machine-like.

Another level to speech is that of the accents and inflexions which depend upon context. More time is taken up in controlling the process if the grammar has to be examined and understood as the utterance proceeds. There are some very good synthesisers on the market, but none of them can really solve this problem to our satisfaction. Some of the very expensive ones come near, suggesting that we are close to solving the problem.

Speech recognition is, of course, the deepest problem in this area. It was hoped that the ability to synthesise speech would automatically lead to a solution to recognition. However, speech recognition is yet another example of the human feature of pattern recognition which is so difficult to emulate in the fields of vision and touch.

There are some simple recognition systems which can understand a few words, when either the person speaking has learned exactly how to say them, or the machine has learned how that speaker speaks. The fundamental processes of the mechanism are still not understood, and it would seem that we must wait for some kind of breakthrough before the problem is near solution.

Movement

To many people this is the main field of endeavour for robotic experiments. It includes locomotive movement, by wheels or leg-like appendages, as well as arm and finger-like devices which can grasp, turn and wield tools of various kinds.

This field is a natural one for experiment, because one of our human attributes is the ability to fashion mechanical objects with great accuracy. Now that we can produce movement in many ways, using electronics, we have a perfect medium for applying control to our environment. We are very good at producing fine and accurate positioning of any object, and this is at the heart of any robotic system.

The human body, of course, achieves movement by contracting muscle fibre attached to levers in the form of bone tissue. Machines, at present, emulate the levers which the human body uses, but they utilise electromagnetism for the moving forces. This is so important to robotics that before any electronics is described, the next section describes how electromagnetism can be used to give movement to machines.

Electromagnetic devices

There are many different pieces of machinery for producing movement, and they all depend upon the fact that if you pass a current through an electric wire, it produces a predictable magnetic field. If there is a magnet nearby, it will be attracted or repelled by this field

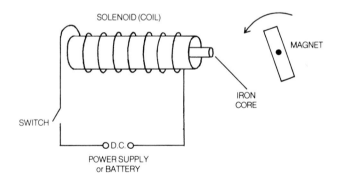

Fig. 1.1. Solenoid.

while the current flows. Switching off the current stops the effect. The strength of the force caused depends upon a number of things, such as the strength of the current, and the exact mechanical relationship between the wire and the magnet. This force can be increased by increasing the actual amount of wire carrying the current. For instance, if the wire carrying the current is wound into a cylinder, the magnetic field along the centre of the cylinder is much stronger than if you just have a straight short wire carrying the current. This type of coil of wire is called a *solenoid* (Fig. 1.1), and if the centre of the cylinder is also filled with magnetic material (iron), the strength of the field at the ends of the coil is further increased.

When the switch is closed, a direct current (DC) flows in the coil, and the magnet suffers a force near the solenoid. This depends upon the orientation of the magnet, the direction of current flow, and the direction of the coil winding. If the magnet is pivoted at its centre, it will rotate to line up in a particular direction, like a compass. Similarly, if the magnet were fixed, and the coil pivoted, and perhaps fed power through a slipping contact, the coil would rotate instead. This type of rotation can be used to move gears and shafts and hence create motion for any type of machinery. The rotating coil is the basis for the small DC motors, powered from batteries, and used for toys and models. This type of motor could be used, for instance, to power the drive wheels of a robot as we shall see in Chapter 3. Another application of the solenoid is in producing 'translational' or backward and forward movement. This is the basis of the magnetic relay. A solenoid is used to attract an iron lever towards it, against a spring, when a current is passed through the coil. This closes a set of switch contacts. When power is removed, the magnet springs back, breaking the switch. We shall see the Spectrum controlling a relay in Chapter 2.

In robotics, one of the main requirements is for accurate mechanical positioning. This is best achieved by a type of motor called a *stepper motor*. Steppers can be made to rotate through accurate, well defined rotational steps, and if connected to a lever or drive wheel through a set of gears will cause accurate movement. The stepper is at the basis of most of the robots on the market, and is easy to control. Chapter 4 shows how the Spectrum can control stepper motors, and will lead on to the control of robot arms.

The rest of this book is devoted to giving you as much information as possible to allow you to experiment and explore various aspects of robotics. Robotics is only in its infancy, and this book introduces some of the most fundamental ideas in the subject. The next section introduces the workings of your Spectrum, to allow you to understand the later projects.

Overview of the Spectrum's electronics

The key to understanding how to interface your Spectrum to control robotic devices is to understand how the Spectrum works. The rest of this chapter is devoted to explaining the internal workings of the Spectrum, and microcomputers in general.

Understanding the Spectrum starts with reading the manuals which come with the machine. The thin introductory manual shows a photograph of the insides of the machine, and you should refer to this now.

The photo itself is actually of the Issue One board, and those with the later (Issue Two) version will have a machine containing rather more electronics. The photo you should be looking at, however, contains enough information for the present purpose.

The board shown is called a *printed circuit board* (PCB). In the past, electronic components would be connected together using copper wire. Today, the copper wires are 'printed' on the surface of a substrate material (fibreglass here) as flat copper tracks. The tracks are then covered with a tin–lead alloy (solder) to protect them from oxidation, and to allow electronic components to be soldered to them. The tracks normally end at holes down which copper is coated to connect tracks from one side to the other. The metal legs of the components also go through some of these holes, and are soldered in place. This type of PCB is termed PTH (*plated-through hole*).

As you can see, the computer consists of many components, with metal legs pushed into the holes of the PCB. After insertion, the component legs must be soldered in place. This is not normally done with a soldering iron in mass production. The PCB, with components on it, is transported over a 'solder-wave', where molten solder is allowed to pass over the under-surface of the PCB, and everything is soldered in place in one fast sweep.

The main components themselves are annotated on the photo, and consist of a number of *integrated circuits* (ICs). Each IC contains many components produced by fine photography onto a small block or 'chip' of silicon. The whole IC chip is then sealed hermetically into a plastic package. Metal legs are formed in the plastic, and connect the chip with the rest of the circuit. It is important to realise that no matter how complex the function of the circuit on the IC, it only has these legs to communicate with the outside world, and everything must pass along them as electronic signals.

Also on the PCB are dozens of *passive* components. These are resistors, for dropping voltages, capacitors mostly used for power supply smoothing, and variable-value resistors and capacitors to allow adjustments to be made to the video picture.

There are also some other important components. Diodes are used for electronic logic purposes as well as for the power supply. Quartz crystals are used to generate very accurately timed clocks. A small coil is used for the power supply, along with an IC for regulating the voltage to other ICs. Other components include a loudspeaker, a UHF or VHF modulator to give signals compatible with your TV, and various sockets to connect external devices to the machine.

Let us now look in more detail, but still in overview, at the entire computer. Figure 1.2 shows an electronic block diagram. There are many interconnections missing from it, but those shown illustrate the main pathways for electronic data, and will be described below. Electronic data actually consists simply of 1s and 0s on electrical wires (or tracks). A 1 level is defined as a +5 V signal, and 0 is at 0 V, or *ground* level. See Appendices 1 and 2 for further information.

There are actually several major internal components of the computer, as follows.

BUS lines

Figure 1.2 shows a number of electronic devices connected together by groups of lines. All the electronic data and control within a computer is nothing more than a pattern of electronic states on electrical wires. Many of the wires do a similar job, and can be conveniently collected together into these groups or *Buses*. A piece of data, which may for instance be an 8-bit binary number in a calculation, or an ASCII code in some text, will inevitably appear somewhere in the computer as a group of electronic signals at some instant of time. In general, all these bits will appear at the same time, in *parallel*, on a group of data lines. If you were fast enough, during the calculation, you could freeze the state of this bus, connect a volt meter to each of the data lines, and read off the binary number as a set of 1s (+5 V) and 0s. In fact, there are special machines made for exactly this purpose, used to repair and prototype new systems. They are called *logic analysers*, because they can display the 'logic states' (1's and 0's) on a group of lines at a given instant of time. This effectively freezes the activity for display and analysis.

Because the bits of the binary number mentioned above appear simultaneously on the bus lines, we say that this is a *parallel bus*, and that parallel communication has occurred. In cases where the bits of the number are sent one at a time along a single wire, we say that *serial* communication occurs.

There are three buses in a typical microcomputer – the *data bus*, the

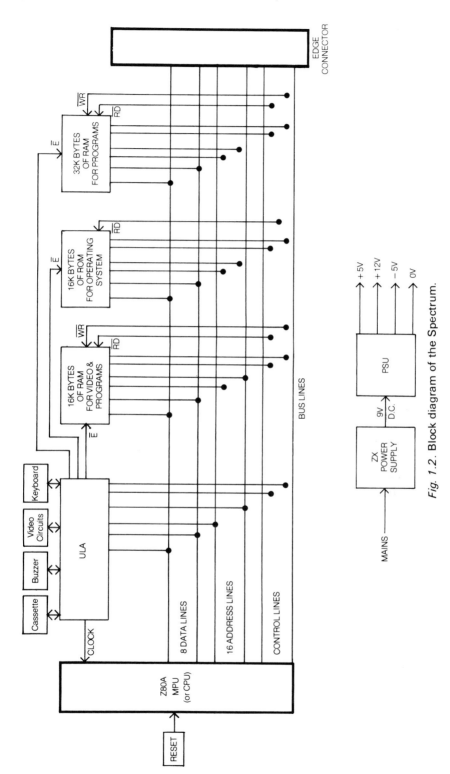

Fig. 1.2. Block diagram of the Spectrum.

address bus, and a rather loose group of lines called the *control bus*. The data bus is 8-bits wide, and the address bus is 16-bits wide. All the devices in the computer are connected to these two buses, and it is important, therefore, that no two devices are active at the same time, or they will clash. Each device has an electronic label or *address*, and this address is passed along the address bus to alert and activate that device alone, when required. It is the job of the MPU to generate this address information, and thus ensure that the correct device is being used at any time. This is further explained when the ULA is described below.

Z80A MPU

This is the microprocessor itself, and is the brains of the computer. It is sometimes called an MPU (microprocessing unit) and sometimes a CPU (central processing unit). Its main attribute is simply that it can fetch instructions from memory, as binary data via the data bus, and execute them in a sequential fashion. This set of instructions is called a *'program'*, and the actual fetching from memory is one of the most fundamental activities which can occur in the machine. It provides an example of parallel transfer of data, and once again is just a question of controlling a set of bus lines to attain the necessary logic states at the right time.

The MPU chosen for a system determines both the electronics and the way in which the machine operates. The Z80 is typical of 8-bit MPUs, and learning about this device will teach you a lot about other MPUs too. The Z80 is said to be an 8-bit MPU as its data bus is 8-bits wide, and hence it can fetch 8 bits at a time.

To fetch data and instructions from memory, the MPU sends out addresses along the address bus, and controls the electronic memory devices by a set of control lines. It expects binary data back along its data lines as a result. The data lines are bi-directional to allow the MPU to store data in the memory too.

Whether the data lines are IN or OUT is determined by the MPU, and it uses two control lines to inform the memory of this fact. These lines are called RD and WR, as shown in Fig. 1.2, and are simply electrical wires which the MPU controls to be in the 1 or 0 state as required. When the RD line is in the 0 state, (i.e. at 0 V), the memory knows that it is to be *read* by the MPU, and the MPU adjusts its data lines to be 'in' lines, ready for this data to be sent to it. When the MPU sets WR to 0, the memory knows it is to be 'written' to by the MPU. The MPU carefully ensures that only one of these lines is low at any instant, to prevent a clash. Note that the symbols for these lines are shown on the diagram with 'bars' over them. This is a convention to inform the reader of the exact action of the line at a glance. It implies that they are active when at a 0 level, and in general when you see a bar over a signal line, it has this meaning. Similarly a line which has a symbol without a bar means that the line is active when in the 1 state.

This explanation of the RD and WR lines has been given as an example of the sort of continuous control which the MPU must maintain over the system. It also shows examples of typical control lines.

Another important aspect of the MPU is the set of instructions which it can execute. These instructions are stored in memory locations as electronic patterns. It is up to the MPU to keep careful track of what it is doing, so that it does not mix these patterns up with data, stored in the same type of memory locations, using the same type of electronic patterns. The exact interpretation of each instruction pattern is decided by the designer of the MPU. The set of 'Operation codes' (op-codes), as they are called, is given as binary or hexadecimal numbers (see Appendix 1). Each such number can be stored electronically, and when fetched by the MPU from memory, causes the MPU to perform a defined set of actions. The language of these op-codes is called *machine code*, and it is perfectly possible for you to learn how these work, and program the computer using them. Machine code programming is a very powerful method of programming a computer, and machine code programs run considerably faster than BASIC programs. However, machine code programming is also very tedious. The Spectrum makes computer programming easier by using a special program called an *interpreter*. This controls the computer and allows the user to input the program statements in BASIC. The interpreter then converts these into machine code, so that the Z80 can understand them.

RAM

RAM stands for *random access memory*, and is a type of memory which may be changed at will, in order to store data and programs. However, when the power is switched off, the contents of the memory are lost. This type of memory is called *volatile*.

Notice that there are two blocks of RAM in the Spectrum. The 16K (bytes) block is the only block found in a 16K machine. The 32K (bytes) block is the addition which turns it into a 48K machine. In the Issue One machine, the extra memory has to be added as a separate PCB of components. On the Issue Two version, you can simply plug the extra memory ICs into the PCB itself.

The 16K block contains the video memory or 'Video RAM', which is written to in order to display data on the TV screen. In addition, the

16K block of RAM contains the special system variables and other pieces of data needed by the computer during its operation. Thus, only a fraction of this RAM is available for your BASIC programs, and data. The 32K block, however, is fully utilised for program and data storage.

You will notice that each RAM block has an electrical line, labelled E with a bar over it (E-bar), and connected to the ULA. This is the 'enable' input for the block of RAM, and when it is in a 'low' state (0 V), only that RAM block is switched on. The ULA sets this pin low when it recognises an address on the address bus which is within that memory block. At the same time, the other blocks are switched off, and in fact are electronically 'unplugged' from the system. This 'unplugged' state is called 'tri-state' or 'high impedance', and the ability of circuits to take on this third state is one of the most important advances in modern computer technology. Because only one memory block is active at any time, and all the other blocks are tri-state, all the blocks may be electrically soldered to the same bus lines without interfering with each other.

ROM

This stands for *read only memory*. It is the same as RAM, except that its contents cannot be changed, and will not disappear when power is removed. The ROM chip is a complete memory block. It also has an E-bar pin which the ULA sets to the active state (low) whenever the MPU puts out an address which is anywhere within the ROM matrix. The chip then performs its own internal address decoding to ensure that data read from it is taken from the correct position within the matrix.

The information within the ROM is called *firmware*, and contains the program which enables the user to input BASIC statements, and execute them as a program. This is the interpreter referred to above. The ROM also contains all the routines which allow the user to operate the keyboard, and read human-readable text from the screen. It is this type of programming which allows a user to program the computer without having any understanding of its internal electronics. The great complexity of electronic control, being performed millions of times per second, is hidden from the user.

The ROM is specially manufactured for Sinclair, and is specific to the Spectrum. It would be impossible simply to plug the same chip into another machine, and use it like a Spectrum. Different machines have different electronics, and hence require different programs for their control. The most important of these differences is in the memory map which will be given shortly.

ULA

This device collects together a whole host of electronics in one specially built IC. ULA stands for *uncommitted logic array*. When a company has designed a large electronic circuit, perhaps containing dozens of ICs, this whole circuit may itself be submitted to a manufacturer of ICs who will then form the entire circuit on a special IC. This is an expensive operation, and can only be contemplated for electronic equipment which will be produced in very large numbers indeed. Your Spectrum qualifies for this type of treatment for a number of reasons. First, it is manufactured in large quantities, and second, it has to be sold at a low price. Committing a large grid of electronics to a ULA saves a lot of money in the long run, if only in terms of assembly and cost. It is much easier to plug a single chip into place than to push many separate devices in and expect them to work perfectly. When a ULA is made, it is also fully tested by computer, thus saving much effort in the final assembly and test.

The ULA performs several functions in the Spectrum, and some of these are listed here.

Address decoding. The ULA performs the essential task of activating the memory block which the MPU wishes to contact from instant to instant. If the MPU wishes to contact, say, the video memory, in order to place something on the screen, it first puts the video memory address on the address bus as a 16-bit binary number. This particular pattern of +5 V and 0 V levels then activates internal circuitry in the ULA. The result is that one of its pins goes to 0. This particular pin is actually connected to the memory bank which contains the memory for the screen, and activates it electronically. Once active, the memory bank uses its own internal address decoding to decide, from the address bus pattern, which location within the memory matrix it should activate to receive the data. After this address has been output by the MPU, the data for that location is placed on the data bus by the MPU, and collected by the activated memory cells. The RD line will be high (i.e. in the 1 state), and WR will be 'low' throughout this transaction, to signify a 'write' from the MPU to memory.

Clock. As you can see, it is important to ensure that the activities of the computer occur sequentially in an organised manner. The activities of the computer must be performed according to some timer or *clock*. The ULA supplies this clock to the MPU, which uses it to time all of its activities. The clock supplied to the Z80 is an oscillator which cycles three and a half million times per second. The frequency is said to be 3.5 megahertz (3.5 MHz, for short).

The ULA also supplies a number of other clocks for memory and video, and generally acts as a sort of 'second in command' to the MPU's control of the system.

I/O (input/output). The ULA is responsible for the input and output lines which are found on the Spectrum. When the MPU wishes to set the buzzer on, for instance, it simply uses the address bus and data bus exactly as described for memory, and the ULA decodes this electronic information into contacting the buzzer, and switching it on. The same is true for the cassette and the keyboard, and we will see in Chapter 2 that the system can be tricked into controlling a very simple external device, such as a relay or electric light, using an I/O line from the ULA. This will provide the reader with an excellent first example of a control situation.

Video. The ULA controls the screen, using the information which the MPU, and program, have stored in a section of memory called the video memory. The screen is effectively a rather elaborate 'window' into this section of memory. When the MPU is commanded to write the letter A, say, to the screen, all the MPU has to do is to write the ASCII code for A into some position in video memory. The ULA takes care of the actual display of the appropriate 'squiggle' which we all call A onto the surface of the cathode ray tube in the television. The exact position of the A on the screen is decided by the address in video memory to which the A is written. Video memory also stores the colours of the screen's contents, and the ULA is responsible for sending the appropriate electronic signals to your colour TV.

All of this takes a lot of controlling, and would slow the MPU down greatly if it had to cope unaided. In fact, the Sinclair ZX80 and ZX81 computers did not have a special controller for the screen, and the MPU had to do the job all the time. That is the reason, for instance, why the ZX81 screen would disappear when a key was pressed – the Z80 MPU was controlling both video and keyboard, and had to leave the screen to service the keyboard. This is not the case with the Spectrum, nor, indeed, with most other computers you will meet.

The ULA, therefore, relieves the MPU of a number of mechanical tasks which would otherwise interfere with its ability to process the program. The same type of control can be found in other computers, but rarely is all the circuitry confined to so small and economic a space as in the ULA of the Spectrum. It is due to this IC that a machine of this complexity is possible in so small a size, and at such a low price.

Miscellaneous

There are some other blocks shown in Fig. 1.2, and these are now described.

The power supply on the Spectrum consists of two separate blocks joined by a cable. One block (ZX Power Supply) contains a mains transformer, some rectifiers, and a large smoothing capacitor, and sits in its own box. It converts 240 V AC into 9 V DC – the label on the power supply says that it can supply up to 1.4 A of current at 9 V.

The second block PSU (power supply unit) is within the Spectrum, and converts the 9 V DC into a number of different voltage levels: +5 V, +12 V and −5 V. There is no −12 V as misprinted in the pin-out diagram of the Spectrum manual. The pin shown contains an unregulated +12 V level.

The +5 V is the most important supply, as this is the normal supply for logic ICs, and simple types of external circuitry. The +5 V supply within the Spectrum, however, is very heavily loaded in the 48K version of the machine, and should not be used for external circuitry. The 16K version does allow some external current capacity, but should not be used too heavily. A separate power supply is described in Chapter 2.

Figure 1.2 also shows a RESET block attached to the MPU. RESET is an electrical pin on the MPU which causes it to start executing from a specific area of memory when the machine is switched on. When electronic components of any complexity are turned on, their internal state is a matter of random possibility. You cannot be sure that the MPU will start executing from the start of the controlling program in the ROM, as power comes up. It may find itself branching off, and executing some random closed and infinite loop. To prevent this, all MPUs have a RESET pin which is normally brought 'low' (i.e. to a 0) soon after switch-on to force the MPU to take on a known and controllable state. It would be inconvenient, and sometimes impossible, to insist that the user should press a reset button each time the machine is switched on. For this reason, a very simple automatic power-on reset circuit is included on all computer systems. The reset circuit simply holds reset low for a set time after switch-on, to ensure that the power supply has come fully up before reset is taken high, and normal execution begins.

The Z80, in fact, starts execution from the lowest address in memory as soon as reset goes high, as long as the power supply has stabilised. Thus the ROM, which must capture the MPU's attention immediately, is set up to occupy the first 16K of the memory's addresses, and is automatically the first thing that the MPU 'sees' after reset.

Another important component of the Spectrum is its expansion edge connector. This allows the user to gain access to all the bus lines of the MPU, along with one or two other useful signals. By constructing interfaces to plug into this edge connector, you can expand you Spectrum in any way you wish. This book is devoted to methods of using this expansion connector for various control and robotic applications. You could just as well use the connector to add on disk drives, extra banks of memory, extra video screens and so on. Of course, the software required for such sophisticated devices is so complex that one would really need a larger computer system for their development. The applications in this book, however, require just the Spectrum, and some fairly simple electronic constructions.

Memory map

Another important concept is the *memory map*, or list of addresses, which various parts of the computer occupy. An understanding of the memory map of the machine allows one to expand it at will, without interfering with devices already present.

The Spectrum manual shows a detailed memory map of the machine, but is more orientated towards software than hardware. Table 1.1 shows a less detailed map, but one which the hardware designer requires for an understanding of the machine.

The map shown is just for memory, but the Z80 MPU actually has a separate I/O address map. This will be described later to allow you to add I/O devices to the Spectrum. It is up to devices connected to the buses to distinguish between these two maps, and there are two control lines output by the MPU to ensure that these devices react correctly. The two control lines are the IORQ and MREQ lines, and they stand for 'I/O request' and 'memory request' respectively. They are similar in many ways to the RD and WR lines described above. When an address on the address bus is meant for a memory device, MREQ is put into the low state by the MPU, and IORQ is held high. Similarly, when an address is for the I/O map, IORQ is low, and MREQ high. An understanding of the RD, WR, IORQ and MREQ control lines, plus the use of the address and data buses, is all that is required for expansion, control and robotic applications. We will see how these lines may be connected up to experimental electronics later.

The memory map shown is labelled both in decimal and hexadecimal, and for an understanding of these, you should consult both your Spectrum manual, and Appendix 1 at the end of this book.

Table 1.1. Memory Map for the Spectrum.

Address band in Hex	(Decimal)	K of store and type	Use
FFFF	(65535)	32K RAM	Available for BASIC programming and variable storage.
8000	(32768)		
7FFF	(32767)	(end of 16K version) 9.25K RAM	Available for BASIC programming and variable storage.
5B00	(23296)		
5AFF	(23295)	6.75K RAM	This block of RAM is devoted to video.
4000	(16384)		
3FFF	(16383)	16K ROM	This block contains the operating system.
0000	(0)		

Remember that the hexadecimal numbers tell you directly what binary pattern is output on the electrical lines of the address bus, in order to activate the various different memory devices in the computer. The address bus lines are labelled from A15 down to A0, and the hex address on these lines is converted to 1s and 0s as in the following example. The address A5BC, using the table in Appendix 1, would come out as:

A15	A14	A13	A12	A11	A10	A9	A8	A7	A6	A5	A4	A3	A2	A1	A0
1	0	1	0	0	1	0	1	1	0	1	1	1	1	0	0
	A				5				B				C		

This pattern of 0s and 1s would appear on the address bus, from the MPU, at just the right time to be collected by the address decoding and memory, so that the data would either be written to, or read from address location A5BC. The timing of this event is taken care of by the MPU, using the appropriate control lines. We will see how to utilise this in a later chapter. Note that there are 16 address lines, giving a total of 2 to the power 16 possible binary patterns, or 65,536. This is referred to as 64K of memory.

I/O map

Of much more importance to the reader of this book is the I/O structure of the MPU. The Z80 has 256 special 8-bit memory locations, called *I/O ports*, which are independent of the memory map shown in Table 1.1. These I/O ports are contacted by a special set of program instructions. To read and write to I/O ports, the BASIC keywords IN and OUT are used, just as PEEK and POKE are used to read and write to memory locations. Each port has an address, and uses the normal address and data bus lines. However, when an I/O port is being used, the IORQ line is at a low level instead of MREQ, as mentioned above, and this state may be used to activate external devices. Table 1.2 shows the logic states on the four control lines introduced so far. Remember that these logic states are voltage levels, and can directly activate electronic devices, as we shall see shortly.

Table 1.2. Logic states of the four main control lines.

MREQ	IORQ	RD	WR	*Action*
0	1	0	1	Memory is being read
0	1	1	0	Memory is being written to
1	0	0	1	I/O is being read
1	0	1	0	I/O is being written to

These are the only logic states allowed on these lines, for reading and writing. You cannot, for instance, have both MREQ and IORQ at a low level together, or the memory and I/O devices would be trying to use the data bus at the same time.

The 256 I/O ports of the Z80 are decoded using the lower eight address bus lines A7–A0, just as memory locations are decoded. However, the Spectrum uses the 256 Z80 ports rather inefficiently, and actually ties up A0–A4, leaving just A5, A6 and A7 free for external address decoding. This only allows eight separate ports to be decoded. However, as each memory or port location has eight bits, one for each data bus line, there are 8×8=64 bits of I/O for external use. Each of these

64 bits can switch a single switch or take in the state of a single bit of input. This is adequate for a small robotic or control application.

Conclusion

This chapter, along with the first two appendices, will have introduced enough ideas for you to understand and try out the experiments and projects described in the remainder of this book. Much of this information is quite general and will allow you to understand microcomputers and electronics for other systems too.

Electronic control, as you will see shortly, is a matter of using the MPU to send electronic signals to the outside world, via its buses and I/O ports. You can control those signals by some very simple programming, and the outside world devices must be connected to the computer according to a set of rules which depend upon the design of the MPU, and the computer system of which it is a part.

Chapter Two
A Simple Control Example

Introduction

This chapter explains how you can hook up your Spectrum to control a simple electronic device. A minimum amount of extra electronics is used, as the project uses the existing electronics of the Spectrum to decode an I/O port. It will give you a feel for the type of programming and electronic construction which is required in this field. However, you will have to open up the Spectrum's case, and make a simple connection to a point on the inside. This is quite straightforward, but if your Spectrum is new and you do not wish to invalidate the guarantee by opening the case, you should still read carefully through this chapter as its main aim is to introduce you to a number of important concepts used in the rest of the book.

It is assumed that you have read Appendix 2, and either that you already know how to construct electronic devices, or that you have tried the practice examples in that appendix. Appendix 4 gives you some suppliers to help you locate the electronic devices required.

The experiment described here will allow you to control an external electronic device, but does not use any input, other than the keyboard. You can use this, for instance, to switch on electronic motors and lights on a model railway, or even to control a central heating boiler, or its pump, according to the time of day – the Spectrum can act as a 'real time' clock. Similarly, you could switch lights on in an unoccupied house, for security reasons. However, the control of mains devices is not described here, and is not recommended without a considerable degree of experience with electrical circuits.

There is nothing very complex about this control, and you would not normally use as complex a device as a Spectrum to achieve it. However, it introduces some invaluable concepts, and gives a simple start to control theory.

The next step, after this example, is to allow some automatic input to the machine, which enables the control to act according to some outside stimulus. Input could also be achieved via the Spectrum's internal electronics, but you would have to lift the lid and solder more wires to the inside for this to be used. The next chapter explains how to expand the Spectrum for input and output, using the rear edge connector. You will be shown how some straightforward electronics can give you many lines for your Spectrum to control, in parallel.

While constructing the projects in this chapter, and in the rest of the book, there are one or two important rules to observe. For instance, never connect anything to any electronics with the power on. You should also be very careful not to short wires and pins together inadvertently while probing around a working device looking for signals of a particular type. You should concentrate continually while you are using electronics, or you will destroy the devices with great ease. If you take every precaution, and keep your wits about you all the time, you will enjoy many hours of highly profitable interest from electronics, and may even find yourself hooked on it as a career!

Finally, you should not begin any of the work until you have read through the entire chapter, and are sure that you understand enough to know what you are doing.

I/O on the Spectrum

Figure 2.1 illustrates a small part of the circuit diagram of your Spectrum. The components are numbered or described according to the Spectrum's convention, and you should refer to Appendix 2 if you require an explanation of the symbols used. This diagram shows how the buzzer, MIC and EAR lines are connected to the ULA. The ULA governs the Spectrum's I/O devices, and here you see how some of them are controlled. This is a clever way of controlling a number of things from a single line. As we shall see, the line (pin 28 of the ULA) is actually contacted at I/O port 254 (decimal).

All I/O ports have 8 bits, and the MPU assumes that each bit is connected to a data bus line. Let us examine port 254. The ULA recognises this address when it appears on the address bus, and takes in the byte on the data bus. Each bit of the byte on the data bus is used by the ULA to switch on or off a particular device within the Spectrum. This means that port 254 is not available for use by external circuitry. The following table gives the use of each bit for port 254:

Bit 7	Bit 6	Bit 5	Bit 4	Bit 3	Bit 2	Bit 1	Bit 0
–	EAR in	–	Buzzer	MIC	Border		Colour

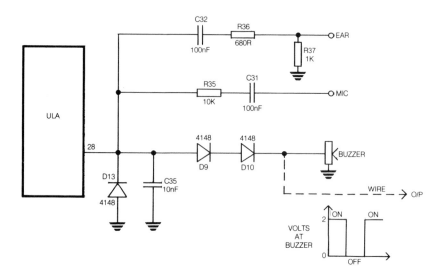

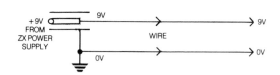

Fig. 2.1. I/O using the ULA.

If bit 4 is set to a 1 in the byte sent along the data bus, the buzzer is turned on. It may be turned off again by sending any byte which has bit 4 as a 0. The MIC is turned on and off in the same way using bit 3. Border colour may be changed by the bit pattern in bits 0, 1 and 2. EAR is actually an input, and is not affected by the byte sent. However, if an IN 254 is typed in, the state of bit 6 is read by the MPU, and can be used to input the state of the earphone output signal from a cassette.

From Fig. 2.1, you can see that pin 28 of the ULA is used for three different I/O devices. It is the bit pattern of the actual data byte sent to port 254 which determines the state of these devices. For instance, as explained above, the statement:

```
OUT 254,16
```

would set the buzzer output to a high level, because 16 is decimal for the binary 00010000. This shows that all the bits, apart from the buzzer bit, are low. Thus, for instance, the border colour would have turned to black.

Sorting out the output lines

If you look at Fig. 2.1, you see that EAR, MIC and buzzer all come from the same pin (28) of the ULA. How does the machine distinguish between them?

Pin 28 of the ULA is electronically both an input and an output. It is controlled by the ULA depending upon the state of RD and WR, which in turn are activated by using IN or OUT statements respectively. EAR, therefore, does not apply when using OUT, and the others do not apply when using IN. However, they can interfere with each other, and you should already know that you cannot SAVE a program with both EAR and MIC connected. The MIC line from the Spectrum to the cassette carries signals to save programs on tape. The EAR line from the cassette to the computer feeds signals into the computer, from tape, for loading programs. However, when saving programs, most cassettes actually feed the MIC signal back along the EAR line. This interferes with the signal going out on the MIC line, at pin 28. LOADing is unaffected, however, as the cassette's MIC connection is inactive during playback.

The ULA distinguishes between buzzer and MIC outputs in an ingenious way. When the MIC output is switched on or off, using bit 3, the ULA outputs a voltage which is either 0 V, for a 0, or just 1.4 V for a 1. The output required to the MIC is an AC signal, and is produced by switching bit 3 on and off successively. These AC oscillations pass through C31, while steady or DC voltages are blocked. Only a small oscillating voltage is required for a MIC input to a cassette recorder, and this small AC voltage, between 0 and 1.4 V, is sufficient. However, this low voltage is not enough to pass through the diodes D9 and D10 and switch on the buzzer, and this device remains off.

When the buzzer bit (bit 4) is activated, the ULA outputs a larger voltage, about 3.3 V, which passes through the diodes and arrives at the buzzer with a voltage of just under 2 V. This explains why the buzzer is so quiet. 2 V is rather low, and if this could be boosted up to 5 V, say, the buzzer would be significantly louder. This can be done, but you would have to cut a track on the Spectrum's PCB, and insert a transistor amplifier in series with it.

Note that when the buzzer is sent an oscillating voltage, this also appears at the MIC. There is no way to stop this.

This explains how we can produce a single output line – simply connect it to pin 28 of the ULA. Setting bit 4 of port 254 high will turn the line on (at 3.3 V), and resetting (low) will turn it off. The next sections show you how to use the buzzer signal as an output, and how to control a relay from it.

The output line

As you can see from Fig. 2.1, there is a problem in using the EAR or MIC sockets to connect external devices to pin 28. There are two components in the way. The resistor is not so important. This does attenuate the current available, but only a small current is needed to switch on a transistor or an IC, and hence control an output. The main problem is the capacitor – C32 or C31. These capacitors block DC signals, and will only pass changing voltages, or AC. When pin 28 is switched on, the voltage changes at pin 28 from low to high, and while this is changing, the capacitor allows this through. However, when the change is complete, the EAR or MIC connection will return to a DC equilibrium level which depends upon the components connected to the socket. The capacitors make it very difficult to connect external circuitry to MIC and EAR, and for this reason we would do better to take a wire from pin 28 itself. However, as explained above, the pin does not give a full +5 V when switched on, and this can be a problem for the electronics we wish to use.

Figure 2.1 shows that at the buzzer itself, after D9 and D10, there is a 2 V swing from logic 1 (on) to 0 (off), produced by bit 4. This is actually quite sufficient for driving the transistor described later, and rather than connecting to pin 28 itself, this is where our buzzer output wire inside the Spectrum's case will be soldered. It is particularly accessible and easy to identify, and the diodes provide some protection for the ULA.

In addition to the output line, Fig. 2.1 shows a power supply connection. The +9 V into the Spectrum is a useful source of power, and will be used to power the circuit after passing through some suitable circuitry.

Boosting the 2 V level to +5 V

Figure 2.2 shows a circuit for turning the 0 V and 2 V of the buzzer wire into +5 V and 0 V, respectively. The buzzer wire is connected through a resistor (10K) to the base (b) of a transistor. The transistor is simply an electronic switch. When its base is fed a small positive voltage, through the 10K resistor, it switches on, and connects its collector (c) to its emitter (e). When this happens, the O/P wire goes to 0 V, or a logic 0.

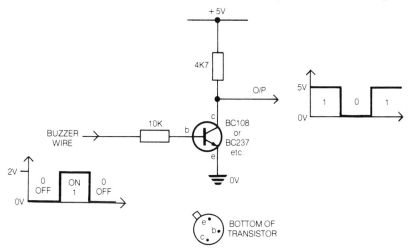

Fig. 2.2. Amplifying the buzzer O/P.

When the transistor is off, i.e. its base is at 0 V, the O/P is pulled up to +5 V by the 4K7 resistor shown, and thus takes on a logic 1. Note that this is the inverse of the input to the base. When the buzzer wire is at 0 V, the output is high, when the buzzer is at 1, or 2 V, the O/P is low. It is up to the program to send out a 0 from the buzzer when a 1 is required on the output of this transistor amplifier. The circuit shown forms part of the project described later. You can pulse this O/P on and off simply by pressing any key on your Spectrum. Every time you press a key, the buzzer gives an audible 'click'. This is the sound of a 2 V pulse being applied to the buzzer, and the amplifier here will turn this into a full 5 V logic level pulse.

The construction and use of the circuit will be described shortly. In order to use it, you will need a power supply for the +5 V shown in the diagram. This is explained next.

A simple power supply

The edge connector of the Spectrum has a +5 V supply pin, but in the 48K Spectrum this supply is so heavily used that there is very little capacity left. You are not advised to use it for projects. However, if you have a 16K Spectrum, you can power this project directly from the +5 V on the edge connector, but a separate power supply is always preferable.

Figure 2.3 shows a power supply which uses a voltage regulator IC (7805) to ensure that the +5 V produced is stable. This is the same IC as the Spectrum uses, and is powered from the +9 V coming from the ZX power supply. There is not a large amount of spare capacity on this supply, but it suffices for small projects. Later on we will see a mains powered supply which you can build.

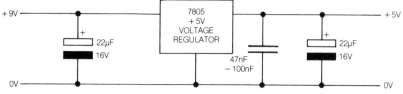

Fig. 2.3. Simple power supply.

The other components used in Fig. 2.3 are capacitors. You will need two types of capacitor, electrolytic capacitors (22 microfarads or more, at 16 V working minimum), and a ceramic disk capacitor (anything from 47 nF to 100 nF). The electrolytic capacitors act as reservoirs to prevent voltage loss when there is a sudden surge of current, and the ceramic is to remove the very high frequency electronic noise. This is very important when powering ICs in later projects, and you should add another ceramic disk as close as possible to the power supply pins of each IC, and with the shortest possible wires.

Power supply construction

Figure 2.4 shows the construction of the power supply on standard 'strip-board' or Veroboard. This board has a matrix of holes at 0.1 in spacing, and copper strips along the undersurface of the board to solder components to. The board is shown from the top, or insulating side, and all the component wires are pushed through from the top, and soldered beneath the board. The copper strips can be used for the interconnection throughout the circuit. Some of the strips must be cut to prevent too many connections, and possible shorting out. This is indicated by crosses in the places where the copper is to be cut. You should cut this at the holes, where the copper is at its narrowest, using a large diameter drill bit, or a special cutting tool which you can buy.

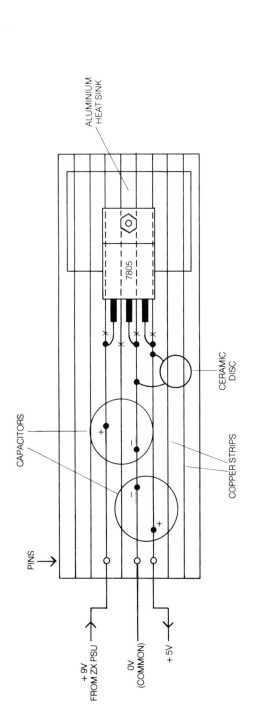

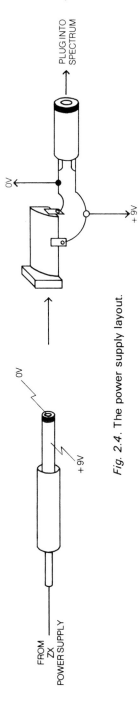

Fig. 2.4. The power supply layout.

Each such cut should be inspected with a magnifying glass to ensure that it is complete.

As shown, the 7805 regulator has three pins, and a metal tab with a hole in it. The metal tab is connected to the middle pin, which is connected to 0 V in Fig. 2.4. The tab is for the removal of heat, and the regulator should be bolted down by this tab to the board. Heat removal from the regulator is further aided by placing an aluminium plate or 'heat-sink' between it and the board.

The electrolytic capacitors shown are the radial type. If you can only find the axial type, these are perfectly acceptable. Just make sure that any electrolytics you ever use are connected the correct way round. The actual values of these components may be anything from 22 μF upwards, at a minimum working voltage of 16 V. Try not to use physically large and cumbersome components. This will keep your construction as neat as possible. The ceramic capacitor can be connected in either way round, but keep its wires short.

The input and output voltages to this board should be connected to Vero pins inserted into the board's holes, and soldered in place as shown.

This board must now be connected to the Spectrum, and the connectors required are shown in Fig. 2.4. The ZX power supply has a lead which plugs into the Spectrum, and you can intercept this with your own plug and socket. You should purchase the same type as used on the Spectrum, and connect the socket up to the plug as shown. The ZX power supply then plugs into your socket, and this connects to your own plug which will fit into the Spectrum's power input. Make sure you connect this the same way round as for the plug on the ZX power supply, and be careful to ensure that your power supply leads have the minimum of bare wire showing. This will help to prevent them from shorting together and damaging the power supply.

Another method of connection simply uses the Spectrum edge connector, to which the +9 V from the ZX power supply is fed. This can be seen in Appendix 3, which describes the edge connector.

When the power supply is complete, you should inspect every joint, and every copper strip to ensure that there is no cross-connection between nearby conductors. The circuit should then be powered up, and the output checked with a multimeter to ensure that it gives +5 V.

Controlling a relay

To switch on motors, lights, models, etc., it is necessary to make some electrical switch contacts close. You do this every time you press down a light switch, or turn on a TV. The computer can produce logic voltages, and some external electronics must turn this into actual switch closures. A common method of achieving this is to use an electrical *relay*. This is a device containing a mechanical switch, which is closed magnetically when a current is supplied to a coil of wire (an electromagnet) in the relay. This section shows you how to turn logic changes ($+5$ V and 0 V) into switch closures.

Again, a transistor is used for the purpose. It is used to turn logic voltages into current for the relay coil. Figure 2.5 shows a circuit for doing this.

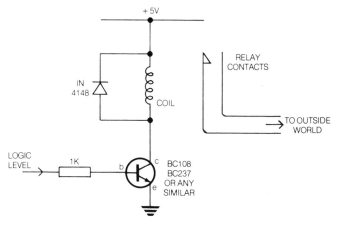

Fig. 2.5. Relay control.

The transistor is switched on by applying a 1 logic level to the 1K resistor in series with the base (b). The transistor again acts as a switch, and when switched on connects its collector (c) to its emitter (e), which is connected to 0 V. This causes current to flow in the relay coil shown, and pulls the contacts closed. The diode shown (IN 4148) is a special protection diode. Whenever you switch a coil on, it acts like a generator for a short time, and can send a voltage spike back to the transistor which may go negative. This spike could destroy the transistor, and is removed by the diode.

The relay contacts form a simple electronically controlled switch, and are the final link in the chain from the software of the Spectrum to the outside world. You can switch anything you wish with these contacts, from low voltage battery devices, to mains. If you need very high power indeed, you can connect them to another higher power relay coil, and switch that on. In this manner you can amplify the power switched as much as you need.

The next section shows you how to build the full output circuit.

Building the output circuit

Figure 2.6 shows the full circuit diagram. There are two transistors, one to change from 2 V to 5 V, and the other to convert this into current for the relay. It is possible to combine these two stages together, but it requires more current to be drawn from the buzzer wire, and is not recommended. The second transistor, operating the relay, gives a good general circuit which we will use again later for converting logic levels to relay drive.

Figure 2.6 also gives a complete layout for the construction. As you can see, there are six components altogether, with their pins pushed through the holes in the strip-board, and soldered underneath. Note that the diode in Fig. 2.5 is not required, if you use the relay mentioned in the component list below, as it is included within the relay housing. It is important that the relay is connected the correct way round, or the diode will short out the coil.

The following is a component list for the board, with identifying marks and standard markings.

Qty.	Item	Markings	Special notes
1	10K resistor	BROWN BLACK ORANGE	Quarter watt 5% resistor.
1	1K resistor	BROWN BLACK RED	Quarter watt 5% resistor.
1	4K7 resistor	YELLOW PURPLE RED	Quarter watt 5% resistor.
2	BC108/BC237 transistor	See Appendix 2	Any general purpose NPN switching transistor.
1	500 Ω 5 V relay plus DIL socket		A relay with minimum working voltage around 3.5–5.5 V will do. The resistance should not be much lower than 100 Ω for the best effect. Type RS 348-582 is shown.
1	Strip-board		Veroboard, 0.1 in pitch holes.
1	Pack pins		Vero pins for external connection.
	Wire		Insulated solid Cu tinned on board, multi-strand for external connection.

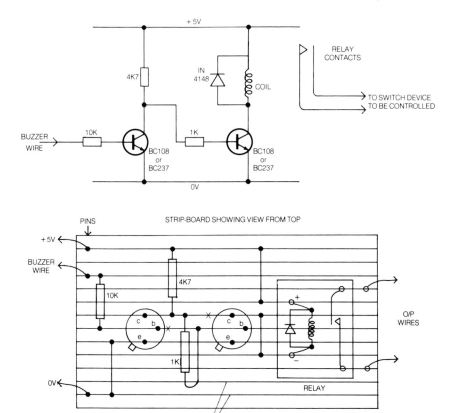

Fig. 2.6. The output circuit.

All these components are easily available, and you do not need to stick rigidly to the exact physical versions stated, though you should only buy alternative electronic types if you are advised by the component supplier that they are equivalent. If in doubt, and if convenient, you should take the circuit into a supplier and show him what you require.

The copper tracks on the strip-board are used mostly to solder components down, to keep them on the board. They will also be able to form some of the connections throughout the circuit. Where these are not sufficient, extra lengths of insulated wire are used. You will find plastic insulated solid tinned copper wire to be most convenient. These wires should be measured against the board, cut and stripped, and then pushed through from the top of the board. Do not use excessive length, or the board will be messy and difficult to troubleshoot if it goes wrong. Similarly, keep the component wires as short as possible, to prevent any cross-connections. It is worth using some insulating sleeving if you have any. All components should be pushed through from the insulated side (top) of the board, to the copper strip below, and soldered. Any excess wire should be neatly clipped off close to the board.

Sockets are available for the particular relays shown. You should always use sockets, as it allows you to reuse components with ease, and helps in replacing faulty ones.

As for the power supply described earlier, when the copper strips connect unwanted portions of the board, they should be cut to prevent the connection. Crosses show suggested cuts in the tracks. Check the cuts with a magnifying glass to ensure that all the copper has been removed; this is a common source of error.

The transistors illustrated are metal can types, with a small tab at the base of the can, for orientation. If you can only find the plastic types, make sure you ask for the pin connections at the same time, as these vary considerably from type to type.

You do not need to stick firmly to the layout shown – use it as an example to produce your own layout, depending upon where you would like to fit the unit. You may have a spare plastic box or case, which will need a different size or shape of board. You only have to make sure that all the connections shown on the circuit diagrams are made, and you can build it in any way you find most convenient. You can even build the power supply on the same board, if you wish.

Testing the circuit

The circuit should be tested before connecting to the Spectrum. Check through the wiring carefully one last time, and inspect again for any shorts or solder flashes, and then connect up the tested power supply.

To see the relay switch over, simply connect the buzzer wire end of the 10K resistor to 0 V. This should switch on the relay. Connection to +5 V will ensure that it is off. If this does not work, you will have to switch off and check through again from the beginning.

If you have a model or a battery powered electric light you wish to control, you should connect it to the relay now, and test the whole system before plugging into the Spectrum. This will allow you to control and test the device by hand.

Connection to the Spectrum

To connect the buzzer wire to the circuit, you will have to open up the Spectrum's case. Turn it over onto a clean surface, and remove the screws recessed into the bottom of the case. Turn the case back onto its base, but be very careful not to split the case open as you turn it over. When the computer is upright again, you can carefully split the case open a very small amount. If you peer inside you will find that there are two very short ribbon cables which connect the top (keyboard) half of the case to the bottom (PCB) half. Do not put any strain on these ribbons, as they push into a couple of sockets on the PCB, and should preferably not be removed. If you do happen to pull them out, they can be pushed back, taking great care not to kink the ribbon. You must make sure they are fully home.

To expose the connection required, orientate the case with the front of the computer towards you, and slightly lift and slide the top (keyboard section) of the case backwards a little way. This will expose the buzzer in the bottom right-hand corner of the PCB. It sits next to the aluminium heat sink bolted to the regulator, and has two connecting pins soldered to the PCB (see Fig. 2.7). The buzzer wire

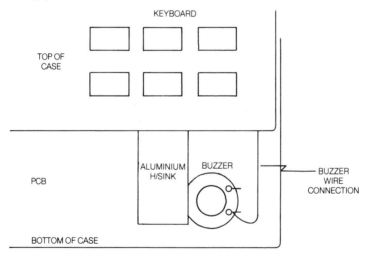

Fig. 2.7. Buzzer connection.

must be soldered to the signal (non-ground) pin of the buzzer. On Issue Two boards this is the bottom pin. You should then lead this wire out under the top of the case to the edge connector slot in the back. The case can then be fitted back together again. Be careful to inspect the ribbons as you close the case, to ensure that they are not squeezed up against anything and kinked. Screw the case back together, and the operation is complete.

The +9 V and 0 V wires can also be soldered inside the Spectrum case at the actual power connector itself if you wish, but make sure you connect them the correct way around or you will damage the circuit.

Using the output board

Assuming that you have checked the system through by hand, it should now be ready to be connected to the buzzer wire from the Spectrum. To see the effect of the experiments we shall try below, you should have a light or some other indicator connected to the relay. You could use an LED, in series with a resistor, as shown in Fig. 2.8, powered from the +5 V supply. Of course, an ordinary torch bulb, or any other electrical device you may wish to control can be used instead.

With the buzzer wire connected, you should be able to switch on the

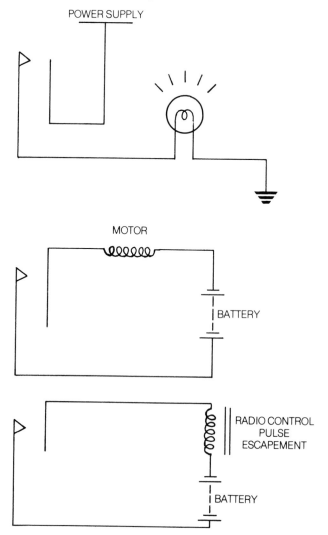

Fig. 2.8. Using the relay switch.

relay by using the programming statements introduced at the start of this chapter. Try running the following program:

```
10 OUT 254,255
20 PAUSE 50
30 OUT 254,239
40 PAUSE 50
50 GOTO 10
```

This program should set the buzzer bit first high, then delay, then low, delay again, and high again. This repeats continuously until BREAK is pressed. Again, if the controller does not follow this sequence, with the relay switching on and off continuously, you must switch off and check thoroughly.

The program shows how the output board works, and gives you your first idea of how a computer can contact and control the outside world. There are many other types of program you can write for this controller. For instance, you can combine the keyboard with a real time clock program to control a model railway signal light. The program should start by asking you what time you want things to happen, and then store these instructions away. As the times come up, the program will switch on the relay, and anything connected to it.

Applications

The prime reason for describing this simple controller is to introduce you to the business of making your Spectrum switch on 'outside world' devices. There are many things you can do with the circuit, and this section suggests one or two.

Figure 2.8 shows three types of device which you might switch with the relay. Electric lights can be turned on and off, again at any time of the day and night, under computer control. This has a number of applications. You might rig up a security light for when you go away. This would simply switch on the light at different times of the evening from night to night, to ward off intruders. At the same time, a cassette recorder could be switched on via its remote input, to create some sounds for further security.

Lights can also be used for other purposes. For instance, if you are interested in the way in which people's reactions are governed, you could ask people to press a key when the light is switched on. This could form the basis of an interesting experiment on the difference between screen-based stimuli and light stimuli. The subject could be asked to react when something is put on the screen in a particular way, and then perform the same task when a light is switched on. The reaction times can be stored in the computer, indexed against name, and called back later for printing or graphical presentation.

There are many variations on this theme, including, say, the way in which sound influences reaction. The relay could switch on a sound, at the same time as a stimulus is given from the screen. The subject could be asked to choose one of a number of options from the screen depending upon the mix of stimuli. Again, the computer is acting as the monitor, collecting all the data automatically. This would form a good technical school's project.

Even though this controller only switches one line, this can be extended to control many more lines by using an 'escapement'. This device is used by radio-control enthusiasts. Essentially, it simply sequences through a set of mechanical stages with each activating pulse. Its main application is in the field of single-channel radio control. Many escapements are simple clockwork motors, with an electro-magnet which moves a toggle-action lever from side to side, allowing the shaft to rotate by, say, a quarter of a turn with each pulse sent to it. By connecting a cam or lever to the shaft, you could use this to close microswitches to control four different things. Of course, to reach any switch, you may have to sequence through all the others first, but this provides no disadvantage for many applications. For instance, in a simple light-based security system you would be able to switch lights on in several rooms according to a sequence. This would make it look as if you were moving around the house.

Applications to model railways or model traffic lights are obvious. You would be able to set up a sequence of timed events, to give your model realism. The major disadvantage of this controller is that there is no feedback from the devices being controlled. This means, in the case of an escapement, that the sequence must be started from a known state, and the computer has to keep track of exactly where it is in the sequence at any time. Also, if there is a problem with the mechanics, the computer will not notice, and can be out of step with the true state of the system.

The next chapter introduces interfaces and peripherals you can add to your Spectrum to allow this necessary feedback. It also shows you how to design your own add-on circuits, using the expansion edge connector of the Spectrum.

Chapter Three
Some Real Interfaces

Introduction

This chapter deals with the type of interfaces and add-ons which are required for control and robotics. Many of the standard peripherals you can buy for the Spectrum use the principles described below, and you will be able to learn enough to understand many of these, and design your own. This has several advantages. First, it can save you money. Second, you will be able to produce just what you need for any project, and understand how it is constructed at the same time. If you can understand how an add-on works, you can use it to the full, and invent new methods of using it to great advantage.

The first project deals with the addition of an LSI I/O chip called a PIO. It is a standard Z80 family device, and almost plugs directly into the Spectrum.

This peripheral gives sixteen bits of input and output, and can be used to interface to many types of robotic and control system.

The example of a simple light-seeking robot mouse is described as a project, and you are shown how to control this with the PIO.

Interfacing peripherals

Chapter 2 showed how external devices can be controlled without any feedback from the outside world. This chapter allows two-way communication with the devices being controlled, so that the computer can give an instruction, and watch the result to allow it to control the event accurately, and intelligently. The first task is to expand the Spectrum to allow inputs and outputs. Chapter 1 showed how some control lines and buses from the MPU are used to alert various devices when they are activated. We will now see how this can be achieved for external peripherals, plugged into the expansion connector. The address bus, the data bus, RD, WR and IORQ will be needed, and you should recall how these work from Chapter 1, if you have forgotten.

Remember that only A5, A6 and A7 are easily available for circuitry added on to the Spectrum, and only these will be required here. Activation of our peripherals will be by using these three address lines, and RD, WR and IORQ.

A parallel I/O chip

This section describes how you can use one of the commonly available LSI ICs to give you sixteen bits of input and output. The IC is called 'parallel I/O', as all the I/O lines from the chip are available in parallel with each other.

Most I/O boards for sale on the market use a single I/O chip. There are many special chips available, and each MPU family normally has a number of them. They are designed to fit straight on to the data, address and control buses with the minimum of interfacing. The common feature of these devices is that they have internal memory locations which are used both as a means of setting the I/O bits, and of controlling the action of the chip itself. The internal memories are called *registers*.

Figure 3.1 shows a diagram of a Z80-family chip called a PIO (*parallel input output*). You should refer to Appendix 2 if you are unfamiliar with ICs, and the standard pin numbering method. There are different speed versions of this chip, according to the frequencies of the Z80's clock. For the Spectrum, you should try to buy the A version of the PIO, which is called a Z80A-PIO. The PIO is a complex chip, and a full appraisal of its function will only come from reading the manufacturer's data. However, it will be shown interfaced to the Spectrum, and its simpler features will be explained to allow you to use it for parallel I/O control.

Figure 3.1 gives the pins which we will need to use, and leaves out several which are unnecessary for the present purpose. There are several familiar labels on the pins of the chip, with eight data bus lines, IORQ and RD control lines. In addition, there are some other control lines, and three lines which we will see connected to the address bus.

There are also two 8-bit I/O ports, called the A-port and the B-port. These pins are labelled PA0–PA7 and PB0–PB7 respectively, and can be controlled to take on logic states for controlling relays, for instance, and hence can be used for controlling the outside world. In addition, they can be used for inputting the state of incoming lines, and in this way allow the feedback loop to be closed.

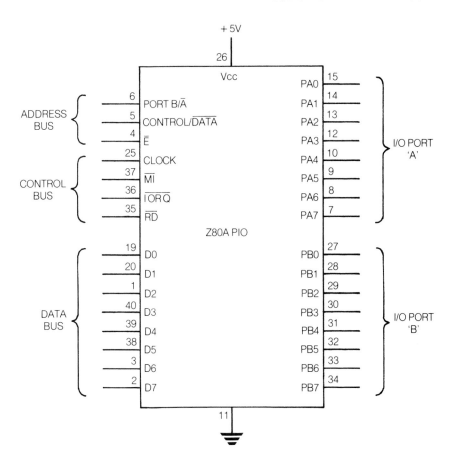

Fig. 3.1. PIO.

Within the PIO there are four registers, as shown in Fig. 3.1. The address bus is used to select these internal memory locations, but they are only to be active when IORQ is low, since this is an I/O device. This is why the PIO is connected to IORQ. Similarly, RD is connected in to tell the PIO whether it is being read from or written to at any time. The data to and from the registers in the PIO passes along the data bus.

Note that the PA and PB lines are labelled in the same order as the data bus lines, along which PA and PB data bits will pass. Thus, for instance, PA0 and/or PB0 will associate with data bit 0 (D0).

PIO registers, and address decoding

Two of the registers within the PIO are called control registers, and they are used to set up the operation of the chip. Each side of the PIO (A-side and B-side) has its own control register. Before the chip can be used, these registers must be written to with one or more control bytes. The other two registers are called data registers, again one for each side, and bits in these registers can be used to set the states of the PA and PB lines of the PIO.

A feature of the PIO is the fact that the control registers can be used to set each individual PA and PB line as either an input or an output. One might, for instance, find that nine inputs are required for a given situation, but only two outputs. One port could be defined as all in, and the other could have one of its lines as in, and the rest as out.

In order to write bytes to the PIO registers, the address bus must be decoded to enable the PIO at some address in the I/O map. This means that when we write an OUT statement, the data in that statement must pass electronically to the PIO when the address bus and control bus are controlled by the MPU to take on the correct states. The PIO takes in control bus lines, and decodes them automatically, but the address bus must still be used to address the chip correctly.

To clarify how this is done, Fig. 3.1 shows, on pins 5 and 6, labels to describe their actions. When pin 6 is high, for instance, it is the B-side of the PIO which is active. When low, the A-side is activated. When pin 5 is high, one of the control registers is being addressed, and when low, it is a data register which is addressed. The address bus lines can be fed to these directly, and this will determine the address of each of the four registers, depending upon the state of the address lines at any given time. (See Table 3.1 below.)

As in the memory blocks described in Chapter 1, the PIO also has an E-bar pin, which must be low for the chip to be active. This can be connected to an address bus line, and completes the address decoding of the PIO. Figure 3.2 shows how to interface the PIO to the Spectrum. All the lines on the left are available on the expansion edge connector, and we shall see how to connect up shortly.

As you can see, A7 is connected to the enable pin, and has to be at 0 to enable the PIO. The table in Fig. 3.2 also shows the states of A5

Table 3.1. PIO address decoding.

	Addresses		Register/action
Binary		Decimal	
A7 A6 A5 A4 A3 A2 A1 A0			
0 0 0 1 1 1 1 1		31	Data to and from Port A
0 0 1 1 1 1 1 1		63	Data to and from Port B
0 1 0 1 1 1 1 1		95	Control Register A
0 1 1 1 1 1 1 1		127	Control Register B

and A6 for selecting the different registers according to the way in which the address bus lines are connected to the PIO. Also, remember that it is a peculiarity of the Spectrum that A4 to A0 must all be 1 when addressing any external circuitry. Table 3.1 gives the addresses at which the registers of the PIO can be contacted. This table will be used below to allow programs to be constructed to control the PIO.

The PIO interface

Figure 3.2 shows the basic connections required for connecting the PIO up to the Spectrum. Some extra components are actually required to control devices, and read back inputs from them. For instance, we shall see how relays can be added to control general electronic devices, as in Chapter 2. First, however, some simple lights and hand-operated toggle switches will be added to the PIO. Switching the lights on and off, and reading the states of the switches, will give you experience in writing programs for the PIO. If you can control and read these simple components, you can control any other electronic devices.

Figure 3.3 shows the extra components. Four of the PIO lines are chosen, two of which will be configured as outputs, and two as inputs. PA0 and PA1 (pins 15 and 14) will be inputs, and are shown connected to toggle switches, to allow you to set their logic states. PA2 and PA3 (pins 13 and 12) are configured as outputs, and are connected to switch transistors on and off. These in turn switch LED lights.

Figure 3.4 shows a layout for the circuit, without detailing every

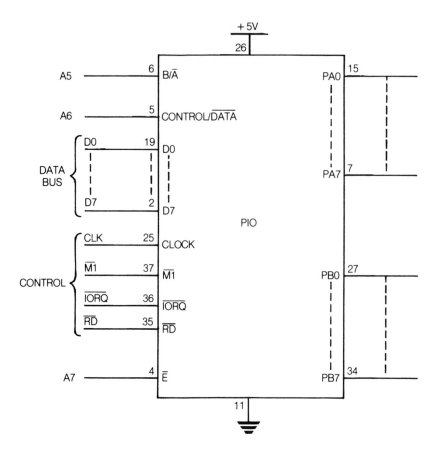

A6	A5	REGISTER
0	0	DATA REGISTER A
0	1	DATA REGISTER B
1	0	CONTROL REGISTER A
1	1	CONTROL REGISTER B

Fig. 3.2. Interfacing the PIO.

single wire which you will have to connect up. You should follow the same general principles as for the strip-board circuits of Chapter 2. Always use sockets for any ICs you may use, and for this circuit you will need a 40-pin DIL (dual in line) IC socket for the PIO. The best wire for this type of construction is called *wire-wrap* wire. It is a very thin solid wire which will not clog up the board. It takes a little

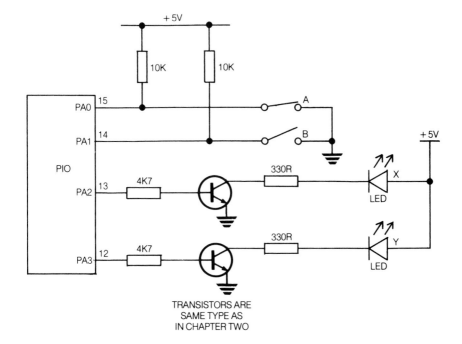

Fig. 3.3. Experiment with a PIO.

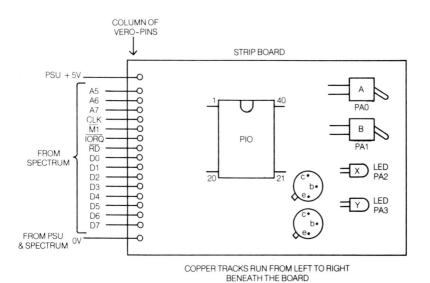

Fig. 3.4. Layout for PIO interface.

practice to strip it, but it is well worth learning to use. You should keep the wire runs very neat, and as short as possible. Do not leave lengths of bare wire either above or below the board. Solder the wire clearly and neatly in place, and clip off any excess. It is very easy to short across tracks with bare wire or flashes of solder in a close situation such as this, and you could destroy your Spectrum if you short out any of its connections. Always check your work with a magnifying glass after soldering each joint, and then find someone else to help you check each connection to ensure it goes to the correct place. This will avoid expensive mistakes later.

You must be careful to cut all tracks which give false connections for the system. For instance, cut all the tracks going to the Vero pins down the left-hand side of the board, as these tracks will almost certainly connect to the pins of the PIO. Also, there will be tracks connecting pins across the PIO beneath the board. These should be cut beneath the PIO. You should follow each track along to ensure that it does not connect two things which should not be connected.

The wires from the Spectrum edge connector will be soldered to the pins down the left-hand side of the board. These pins should be connected to the PIO pins with wire-wrap wire as shown in Fig. 3.2. This is a total of 15 pins, plus a 0 V line, and includes one or two which are not familiar. These are used by the PIO for special internal timing. There is also a +5 V connection to the power supply unit, and the 0 V pin must connect to both the PSU and the Spectrum, to give a common ground line.

The edge connector used to connect into the back of the Spectrum will have to be purchased from a component supplier (see Appendix 4). It must have open ends, and is a double-28-way 0.1 inch pitch PCB edge connector with a slot in the fifth place. Ask for a socket suitable for a Spectrum, and you should have no trouble. Refer to Appendix 3 for a picture of the edge connector, and be careful to connect it up exactly as shown. You should use multi-stranded wire for this purpose, and again just strip enough insulation off for soldering – do not leave more bare wire than is absolutely necessary. The more meticulous you are about the construction, the less likely failure will be. You should not use too long a length of wire for the Spectrum connections, as bus lines are not good at driving their signals over long distances. Four or five inches is quite acceptable.

When complete, and fully checked, you are ready to plug the socket into the Spectrum. Do not insert the PIO in place in its socket yet. If you inspect the edge connector on the PCB at the back of the Spectrum, you will see the tinned copper fingers which your edge-socket must connect to. In the socket, there are spring contacts to hold firmly against the tinned PCB fingers. When you push the socket in place, you must take care to locate it correctly. This will be facilitated by the fact that the slot of the PCB should locate with a tab in the socket at this position. Ensure that this polarising tab is in place. If it is not, be careful that the spring contacts are central to the PCB's tinned fingers, and that they do not land in between them, and short across adjacent tracks.

When you are sure that all is well, place the board on a clean insulating surface, to prevent shorts, and switch on the Spectrum. If the normal sign-on message does not appear, you must turn off immediately, and inspect your work – there will be a short or misconnection somewhere. It must be found before you try again. When all is well, switch off and insert the PIO – never insert or remove an IC with the power on. Switch on, and if the sign-on message appears you may proceed.

Using the PIO

To set up the A-side of the PIO, it is only necessary to send a particular sequence of control bytes to address 95 – the control register for the A-side. Similarly, to address 127 for the B-side. Operation of the PIO can be quite complex, and we shall restrict ourselves to its use as two simple I/O ports.

To set up one of the sides of the PIO, the first step is to write the byte '255' to that control register of the PIO. This is a sort of magic key, and understanding this ritual can only come from reading the data on the chip, which is beyond the scope of this book. The bits of the next byte written to the control register are used by the PIO to determine which lines are inputs, and which are outputs. Where there is a 1, the corresponding I/O bit is in. A 0 sets that bit to out.

For instance, to set all of the PA lines to output, the following is typed in:

```
OUT 95,255
OUT 95,0
```

This writes first 255, then 0 into the control register for the A-side. As decimal 0 is equal to 00000000 in 8-bit binary, all the PA lines are now defined as output. If, for instance, 239, or 11101111, had been written in the second statement above, all the PA lines would have been inputs, except for bit 4, which would have been an output.

The next step might be to send a byte to the data register for the A-side. Those bits in the byte which correspond to output lines will appear on their respective lines, and any that are inputs will not be affected. The following program will set up the A-side entirely as outputs, and then switch on all the A-lines:

```
10 OUT 95,255
20 OUT 95,0
30 OUT 31,255
```

As all the A-lines are switched on by this simple program, this will include the lines connected to the switches. Make sure that the two switches are off at this point, or the switches will be grounding their pins, while the above program is setting the pins to a 1. This will cause a conflict, and may damage the PIO.

Try changing the number (255) which is output to port 31 in line 30, and see the effect on the lights. See if you can turn either of the lights on at will – this is explained shortly. Also, you can read back the last number you sent to the PIO outputs. Thus, if you type in:

```
PRINT IN 31
```

you will find that 255 is printed on the screen after running the program above. Try reading back other numbers as you change program line 30 above.

An IN statement is used to read the states of the input lines. Only those bits of the data register which are defined as inputs will read in data, the others are outputs, and will be read as the state they were last set to. We shall now see how to read the states of the switches in Fig. 3.3.

The switches are labelled A and B, and the LED lights are labelled X and Y, for identification.

The first step is to initialise the PIO by sending 255 to port A's control register (OUT to address 95) followed by a byte to set the lines as in and out accordingly. For the switches and lights shown, we must set the two least significant lines as inputs, and the next two as outputs. Thus the next number (after 255) sent to the control register must have a binary value of the form:

```
x x x x 0 0 1 1
```

x is anything because the PA lines corresponding to these bits are not connected, and hence are irrelevant. Any number having the last four bits as shown will do; for instance 00000011. This number is the decimal number 3.

After sending the two control bytes, the state of the lights and switches can be altered and read respectively at address 31. As the switches are now connected to inputs, they can be switched at will without fear of conflict.

Let us look at the lights first. To switch on light X alone, a 1 must be sent to bit 2, but not to bit 3. This requires a number such as:

x x x x 0 1 x x

Again, x can be anything, and 00000100, or decimal 4, will do. You should check for yourself that 8 will switch on the other LED, and that 12 will switch on both. The most important point is that you have to communicate with just one or two bits for this type of control, using arithmetic, and decimal numbers in BASIC.

To read the switches, the same principles apply. Try running the following program and observe the numbers printed on the screen as you change the switch states.

```
10 OUT 95,255
20 OUT 95,3
30 OUT 31,0
40 CLS
50 FOR I=1 TO 100
60 PRINT IN 31;
70 NEXT I
80 GOTO 40
```

Line number 30 is purely to set all outputs to 0 to ensure that a definite number is returned from those pins. You could set them to any state, but 0 is convenient as the numbers then returned by the above program are small and easy to deal with.

When using a mixture of inputs and outputs, it will not always be possible to set the outputs to a simple state as above. Also, when using a mixture, some analysis will be required to sort out the input bits from the rest, and hence determine the states of those input bits.

As you can see, when a PIO port is read, the number which returns is made up of two primary types of data. Bits which are inputs take on the state of those inputs, and bits which are outputs take on the state of those bits as actually set up during the last OUT statement to that port. In this case, suppose that switch A is closed, as shown, and switch B is open. Also suppose that both lights are lit. The binary equivalent of the decimal number which returns from the following statement:

```
PRINT IN 31
```

would be:

x x x x 1 1 0 1

Because of the uncertainty of the left-hand four bits, the decimal number from the IN statement could be any one of 16 numbers which have 1101 in the right-hand half of the number. The problem is to use BASIC arithmetic to analyse this number, and recognise that switch A is closed, and switch B open. This is an easy task if in binary form, but BASIC works in decimal. The first task, therefore, is to convert the decimal number from an IN statement to binary. Only the two least significant bits are actually needed, and this is straightforward. Appendix 1 shows how to do it using division.

As an example, suppose that reading in from port 31 gives the number 29. The first two steps in the conversion would be as follows:

$$29 / 2 = 14 \text{ remainder: } 1 = \text{bit 0 (state of switch A)}$$
$$14 / 2 = 7 \text{ remainder: } 0 = \text{bit 1 (state of switch B)}$$

This is far enough, and can be used in a BASIC program to analyse the state of the switches. The following program checks the state of the switches continuously, and transfers those states to the LEDs:

```
10 REM *** SET UP PIO FIRST
20 OUT 95,255
30 OUT 95,3
40 REM *** READ SW. STATES
50 LET X=IN 31
60 REM *** FIND LS BITS
70 LET Y=INT(X/2)
80 LET BIT0=X-2*Y
90 LET BIT1=Y-2*INT(Y/2)
100 REM *** IF BIT0=0 THEN
110 REM *** SW. A IS OFF,ETC
120 REM *** NOW SET LIGHTS
130 LET Z=4*BIT0+8*BIT1
140 OUT 31,Z
150 REM *** KEEP REPEATING
160 GOTO 50
```

While this program is running, you can change the switches, and watch them affecting the lights. Line numbers 70, 80 and 90 show you how to compute a remainder, and line 130 is a method of converting 1s and 0s into states of the lights. For instance, if bit 1 is 1, then line 130 will add 1*8 to Z, and this will put a 1 on bit 3 to switch on LED Y.

You should be able to write your own programs based on the above principles, and experimenting with this simple circuit will give you experience in controlling I/O lines in general:

Robot mouse

The robot mouse has been a symbol of the simpler types of mobile robot for a number of years. A simple form of such devices is a chassis with two large drive wheels at the back, and a single steerable wheel at the front. While the mechanics of such devices will be left to you to design as you wish, this section describes their control using some simple electronics for experimentation. This is a good example of a robotic application, as it entails both control of a mechanical device, and feedback from that device to make the control 'intelligent'. You can even experiment with simple learning processes, using the mouse, and these will be suggested below. The principles you will learn from this project will hold good in any robot project you may try in the future, no matter how complex.

Figure 3.5 sketches a possible mechanical set-up. Forward and reverse drive is provided by a DC motor which is shown driving through a crown wheel and pinion type of gear – any other which you can construct from parts bought at a model shop will suffice. Steering is by worm drive from a DC motor to a vertical axis holding a free-running front wheel. On the steering axis is mounted a lever which contacts microswitches at the extremes of the steering travel. The motors which you use decide the power supply which will be required. You can use rechargeable batteries for this application, and mount them on the robot mouse itself. A 6 V battery is typical, but you can use any convenient voltage, depending upon what is available.

Wire will have to connect to the robot mouse from the Spectrum, to carry controls for the motor relays, and any feedback which you may wish to use. In a sophisticated application, the control data could be sent and received by infra-red remote transmitters and receivers – this frees the robot mouse from trailing a connection to the computer.

Figure 3.6 shows a relay circuit for controlling steering and drive. The steering relays have two on/off contacts each, and the drive direction relay is a double-pole double-throw type. All relay contacts are shown with the relay coils de-energised. You should inspect this

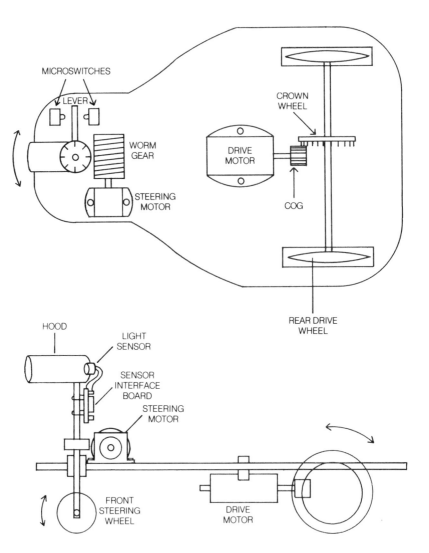

Fig. 3.5. Robot mouse.

diagram carefully before continuing, and imagine the effects of closing and opening the relay contacts shown.

The steering motor is off until one of the relays is energised. As you can see from the diagram, each relay switches 0 V and +6 V to the steering motor connections a different way round. This allows the steering motor direction to be controlled. It is important that only one of these relays is on at any time, as turning on both will short the power supply out. A fuse in series with the 6 V line would be a useful addition to prevent damage in case of a mistake.

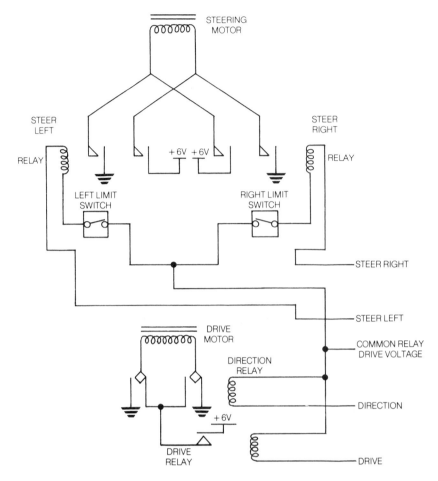

Fig. 3.6. Mouse controls.

If one of the steering relays is left on, the steering eventually reaches its limit, and the appropriate relay coil is switched off by the limit microswitch in series with it. This prevents the motor from overdriving.

The direction and power to the drive motor is controlled by two more relays. The four relays all connect up to a common drive voltage, and this gives five wires to be fed to the computer. The 6 V motor supply batteries are assumed to be mounted on the robot mouse itself, if it is powerful enough to carry them.

To control the robot mouse intelligently, there should be some feedback to the computer. This can be added in several ways. You could fix microswitches back and front to detect when the robot mouse comes up against a solid object – a 'bump detector'. You could monitor the current in the drive motor. When it is trying to push the robot mouse into a solid object, the motor is more heavily loaded, and the current rises as a result. A heat detector could be included to detect heat sources, or a light detector for bright lights. Even sound may be useful in some circumstances.

The feedback chosen here will be a simple light switch which gives a positive indication when light above a certain threshold is incident on the detector. There are standard light detector switches on the market, or you can build one of your own. This will be described next.

Light detection

The best place to mount a light detector is at the top of the steering column, as shown in Fig. 3.5. As the front wheels steer, the light detector swings around to point in the direction the robot mouse is going. Figure 3.7 shows the light cell itself mounted inside a hood to ensure that the cell does not receive too much stray light. You could add a simple lens system to concentrate the light more accurately, and increase the sensitivity and directionality.

There are many types of cell which will give an electronic indication of light level. Two types are mentioned here, but you will find others in general electronic books, and any will do. The LDR (*light dependent resistor*) is one of the oldest types of light detector. It simply reduces in resistance as the light level rises. Figure 3.7 shows a circuit for a standard LDR known as a CDS cell (*cadmium sulphide cell*), along with a typical layout on Veroboard. The ORP12 is the commonest LDR of this type, and is very generally available. Here it is shown connected into a circuit using a special type of integrated circuit amplifier called an op-amp (*operational amplifier*). Again, the commonest variety is chosen for the circuit, and it is called a 741. You can buy this in the form of an 8-pin IC, and the pin numbers shown assume this type.

The flat miniature variable resistor shown has three pins. One of these is called the 'wiper', and in this circuit it is connected to one of its other pins, and to 0 V. Varying this resistor varies the threshold for light detection. The output of the circuit will swing from 0 to 1 as the light level exceeds or drops below the threshold band, making sure that there is no intermediate voltage value to confuse the computer's input. To achieve this, the 741 is connected up in a configuration called a *Schmitt trigger*. The resistor values shown may be experimented with to obtain the best electronic result for the lighting conditions in which you will be using the robot mouse.

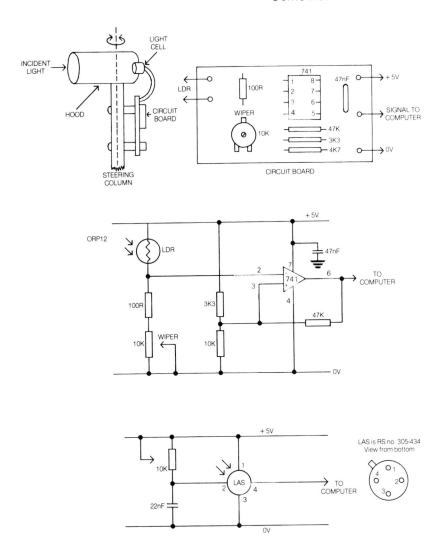

Fig. 3.7. Light switch.

The second type of light switch is based around a complete transistor-type package containing a LAS (*light activated switch*). This device will give a 1 or 0 output depending upon the light level and the threshold set by the 10K variable resistor shown.

The circuit which you decide to use is best mounted on a small piece of Veroboard just below the light cell itself, and you should insulate the undersurface of the board to prevent shorts.

The signal from this board, and the power supply lines to it, come through light stranded wires, to provide the minimum strain on the steering motor's movement. These wires will connect to the PIO board.

Figure 3.8 shows the interfacing of the robot mouse to the Spectrum using the PIO. The relays shown should be 5 V working, with coil resistances of around 100 Ω or more. In order to prevent electronic noise from their action, a 100 nF capacitor should be connected across each one, and a diode as explained in the last chapter – unless the relays come with an integral diode. The transistors are as in the last chapter. Figure 3.6 shows a line called the common relay drive voltage. This is the +5 V line shown in Fig. 3.8, and comes from the PIO board's supply, which should be constructed as explained in Chapter 2.

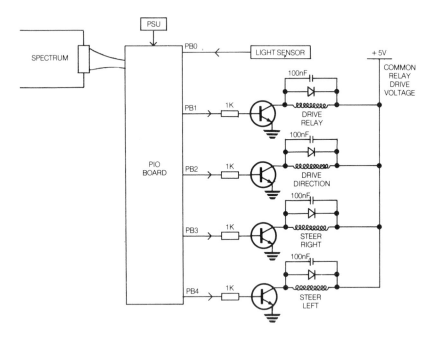

Fig. 3.8. Interfacing the mouse to the Spectrum.

For contrast, this application uses the B-side of the PIO. The light sensor should be connected to PB0, to make its state easy to analyse from the data read back. The relays are activated by high states on PB1–PB4.

Operating the robot mouse

The robot mouse described here is capable of many types of function. Once you are familiar with the basic system, there are many expansions which you can make. However, with the inputs and outputs shown so far, the easiest activity to illustrate is the activity of steering towards a light source.

The first task is to set the light threshold so that the robot mouse can 'see' the light, and distinguish between looking directly at it, and looking away. This is done using the following program, and watching the TV screen.

```
10 REM ** SET UP PIO B-SIDE
20 OUT 127,255
30 REM ** PB0 INPUT, REST OUT
40 OUT 127,1
50 REM SET ALL OUTPUTS TO 0
60 OUT 63,0
70 REM INPUT AND DISPLAY
80 CLS
90 FOR I = 1 TO 100
100 PRINT IN 63;
110 NEXT I
120 GOTO 80
```

As you adjust the variable resistor, you will find a position where shading the light changes the number. When the light switch is thus working correctly, this feedback can be used to control the steering motor.

To switch the relays, numbers are output to port 63. The drive relay is connected to PB1 – this corresponds to bit 1 of the data bus, and the instruction:

```
OUT 63,2
```

will switch the relay on. The following table shows you the numbers which must be output to port 63 for the different functions:

Number output	Action
2	Drive relay on
4	Drive direction change
8	Steer right
16	Steer left

Any of these can added together, except steer right and steer left at the same time, which will blow the fuse on the 6 V power supply. For instance, 2+4+8=14, thus the robot mouse would drive forward, and to the right if:

    OUT 63,14

were typed in. It is up to you to connect up the motors in order to define which relay is steer right, and which is steer left, as well as the direction of the drive motor. It is best, in general, to connect relays so that they are off in the most frequent state. For instance, the drive direction relay should cause the forward direction to be selected when the relay is off. This saves relay wear and power.

You should experiment with turning functions on and off to gain some experience with the method of control before continuing. Note that if the steering reaches its limit in any direction, it cannot be overdriven, but it can be driven back the other way, and off the limit switch.

As there is no feedback from the steering limit switches in this basic version of the robot mouse, timing loops are used when steering. To make the steering column turn to look for a light source, it must be turned back and forth until a high enough light level is detected. This is done by driving the steering in one direction for long enough to ensure that it is against the stop. A loop is executed during which PB0 is continually read until it detects light. A loop counter is also kept. Trial and error will tell you how many counts are necessary to ensure that the steering is at the stop. This depends upon your mechanical set-up. Once the steering is definitely at an end, the steering is reversed, and PB0 monitored again. If no light is detected, this loop will continue unchecked. When light does appear, the steering can be stopped, and drive forward selected. This automatically sets the robot mouse steering towards the light. The robot mouse will move around in an arc, taking the light detector away from the light, and the drive can then be switched off, and the steering and detection repeated. A program to achieve this is given in the next section.

This straightforward function can be improved in a number of ways, and as you experiment with the robot mouse, you will find many refinements to this routine. For instance, when light has been found, the drive could continue, and the steering could be moved from side to side to keep the light in its sights. In this way the robot mouse could be made to steer almost straight to the light.

Programming the robot mouse

Figure 3.9 shows a diagram of the activity described above, in a form called a *flow chart*. It sets out the program in a visual form which is easy to digest and describe. There are three shapes of box used here. The rectangle is the statement box. The diamond is a decision box, and has two exits, labelled 'yes' and 'no'. The first box in the chart, at the top, has rounded ends, and is the start box, and contains the first statement in the routine. You will find that you can follow the flow through with ease, and the following is a description of the process.

The first step is to set up the PIO with the correct in and out lines, and then zero the variable (N) used as a counter in the loops. The next statement is simply to ensure that the drive motor is off. The robot is meant to look for light, and drive towards it, and it starts by turning its steering and light detection to the right. The next box is a decision – if light is not detected, the counter advances, the value of N has not reached 200 yet, and the light continues to be monitored with the steering driving right. This continues until either light is detected, or the counter runs out and the steering is set steering left. The counter has been set to a maximum of 200 arbitrarily, and it is up to you to experiment with counter values which ensure that the steering limit is reached in each direction.

If the counter runs out the steering goes left, and light detection is checked, again using a counter to limit the time for which this function is performed. If no light is detected in this direction after the count of 200, the routine starts again, with the counter reset, and steering set to drive right. This simple routine continues unchecked until light appears.

If light is detected before a counter runs out, the steering is switched off, and the drive set moving forward. Light detection is still checked, and if it disappears, the routine starts from the beginning again, with the drive turned off.

The light detection part of the routine comes from checking the state of PB0. This is done by checking whether the decimal number returned from port 63 is even or odd. If even, then bit 0, and hence PB0 is a 0, and if odd it is a 1. If you have chosen the LDR circuit then PB0 at 0 level means light has been detected, 1 means no light.

The program continues unchecked until you BREAK it yourself, which means that if the robot detects light, it will drive towards it forever, and will not stop when it arrives. You will have to be careful using this simple routine.

The following is a program which follows the flow chart:

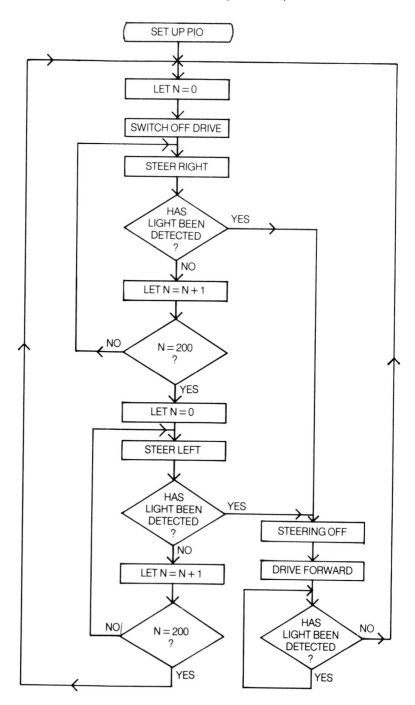

Fig. 3.9. Flowchart for mouse control.

```
 10 ** REM SET UP PIO B-SIDE
 20 OUT 127,255
 30 OUT 127,1
 40 OUT 63,0
 50 REM ** SET UP COUNTER
 60 LET N=0
 70 REM ** STEER RIGHT WITH DRIVE OFF
 80 OUT 63,8
 90 REM ** CHECK LIGHT
100 LET K=IN 63
110 IF 2*INT(K/2)=K THEN GOTO 500
120 LET N=N+1
130 REM ** REPEAT LOOP UNTIL LIMIT REACHED
140 IF N<200 THEN GOTO 60
150 REM ** STEER LEFT AND REPEAT AS ABOVE
160 LET N=0
170 OUT 63,16
180 LET K=IN 63
190 IF 2*INT(K/2)=K THEN GOTO 500
200 LET N=N+1
210 IF N<200 THEN GOTO 160
500 REM ** STEERING OFF DRIVE FORWARD
510 OUT 63,2
520 REM ** CONT. IF LIGHT STILL THERE
530 LET K=IN 63
540 IF 2*INT(K/2)=K THEN GOTO 530
550 GOTO 60
```

The best plan is to study this program, and use it as the basis of your own experiments, rather than simply using it verbatim. For instance, you could add a counter into the final few lines of the program to limit the amount of time for which the robot will seek the light, and hence prevent its driving stupidly into the light itself.

Further refinements could use the real time clock program shown in the Spectrum manual, to command the mouse to perform its activities according to some time frame.

Other refinements include further feedback devices – for instance, two of the bits left over on the PB lines could be used to gain feedback from the steering limit switches, to allow the computer to monitor when the limit has been reached, and not have to use the open-loop control of a timing counter, as above. You would be advised to use PB1 and PB2 for these inputs, and slide the outputs up two bits – it makes the calculation easier.

The project of which this is a basis can be extended as far as you wish into robotics. For instance, as the robot moves about the floor, it could store the values of N, and use these to retrace its steps, or learn a route from the start to where the light was last seen, or even where it usually is.

The best software extension would be to learn and use machine code by buying one of the excellent Assemblers on the market, and controlling the bits in a more direct manner. The program processing speed increase is also considerable, though this is not a major factor as the mouse mechanics will probably be quite slow to react, giving plenty of time for calculation.

Add-ons in general

There are some general principles which you can apply to the design of your own peripherals, based on the PIO interfacing above.

The first principle is that almost all LSI chips have, in addition to I/O lines, a data bus, a chip-enable and/or some internal register selects, and an RD or WR equivalent. In fact, in general, you can make do with just these pins. Some I/O chips, however, have more lines than this, as for the PIO. These extra lines are used for the more complex aspects of the chip's control, and the above few lines will often be sufficient for a simple application.

Figure 3.10 gives an example of a general I/O chip. It may not even be a parallel I/O chip, it may be designed to interface varying analogue voltages to the computer, or serial lines whereby the data is sent one bit at a time. The actual I/O itself is not important for interfacing. If the chip has internal registers, the actual character of the I/O involved is a matter of software, which must read from and write to these registers.

The diagram shows the form of a general peripheral interface. You should be able to use this, and the following explanation, to interface most peripherals to the Spectrum, or indeed to any other computer. The only block which has not been explained in detail so far is the address decoding block. This simply recognises addresses meant for this peripheral, and sets its output line low to enable the peripheral. We will see an example of this later. So far, the circuits we have met (the ULA and PIO) have performed this function automatically, by taking in the address lines directly, and decoding with no extra circuitry.

In Fig. 3.10, IORQ is shown being used to enable the address decoder, to ensure that only I/O commands enable the circuit. The address on the address bus, or some subset of the address bus, is then used to enable the actual I/O chip itself. At the same time, the state of

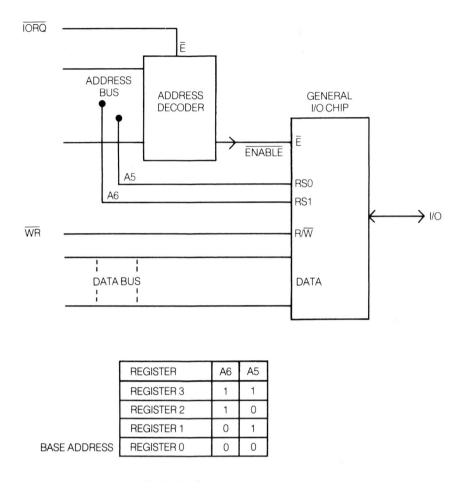

Fig. 3.10. General peripheral.

REGISTER	A6	A5
REGISTER 3	1	1
REGISTER 2	1	0
REGISTER 1	0	1
REGISTER 0	0	0

BASE ADDRESS

WR will tell the chip whether this is an IN or an OUT. WR is shown connected to a theoretical R/W pin. This is a common type of read/write input, and as the diagram shows, if it is a 1, a READ occurs, and if 0 then WRITE. This exactly agrees with the Z80's WR line. Notice that RD is redundant in general, and many microprocessors only have a R/W line, which is equivalent to WR on the Z80.

Once the chip is enabled, the data transfer can occur, but it is essential that the correct internal register is contacted. The diagram assumes that there are four or less internal registers, and these are addressed using the RS1 and RS0 pins, which are connected to A6 and A5. The table shows how different states on A6 and A5 give different registers. The lowest address in the group is called the *base address*, and it is this base address which is determined by the address decoding. In other systems, one would use A1 and A0 as the register selects, to make the address map neater. This is not possible on the Spectrum, however.

The only other connections are the data bus, and power supplies. The power supply is normally +5 V, unless the I/O being interfaced has its own special voltages.

This gives a general idea of interfacing I/O to the computer. Address decoding is described next, along with some electronic logic which can be used for address decoding, and expanding to more than one peripheral at once. For instance, you may require two or more PIOs for a project.

Address decoding

As you will know by now, when your program wishes to switch on a device, it has to send the appropriate decimal number to an output port. We saw in Chapter 2 how setting a bit on port 254 activated an output line. The ULA performed the function of decoding the MPU's control and address bus to ensure that port 254 was activated on time. We will now see how this is done in general.

For instance, to set bit 3 of port 31 to a 1, the MPU sends the bit pattern:

Bit 7	*Bit 6*	*Bit 5*	*Bit 4*	*Bit 3*	*Bit 2*	*Bit 1*	*Bit 0*
0	0	0	0	1	0	0	0

which is 08 (hex), to port 31 along the data bus. To ensure that the receiving electronics at port 31 is activated to receive this bit pattern, the MPU sets the lower eight bits of the address bus to contain the bit pattern 31 (decimal) or 00011111 in binary. At the same time, so as not to be confused with a memory transaction, IORQ is set low (active). Also RD is high and WR low to show that the MPU is writing out data, as opposed to reading the state of the port.

The above set of electronic levels on the address and IORQ lines is unique to the particular I/O chip which is being written to. These levels are only set up for a minute fraction of a second, as the program executes, and hence must be recognised and used by some fast electronics 'on the fly' as it were. The address decoding contains this electronics, and having recognised this unique logic pattern it sets its output low and enables the I/O chip. The activated I/O chip then takes in the pattern of bits on the data bus, which the MPU has placed there while the enabling conditions above are set up.

Figure 3.11 shows a diagram of a typical chip which performs this

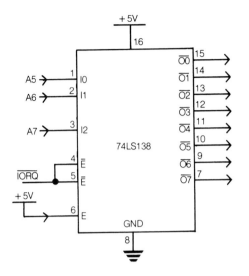

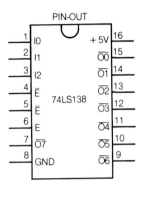

PIN-OUT

TRUTH TABLE SHOWING THE
OUTPUT STATE OF
THE 74LS138 FOR EACH
POSSIBLE INPUT STATE

$\overline{E} = 0$ and $E = 1$

I2	I1	I0	O0	O1	O2	O3	O4	O5	O6	O7
0	0	0	0	1	1	1	1	1	1	1
0	0	1	1	0	1	1	1	1	1	1
0	1	0	1	1	0	1	1	1	1	1
0	1	1	1	1	1	0	1	1	1	1
1	0	0	1	1	1	1	0	1	1	1
1	0	1	1	1	1	1	1	0	1	1
1	1	0	1	1	1	1	1	1	0	1
1	1	1	1	1	1	1	1	1	1	0

Fig. 3.11. Decoding.

decoding of the address bus. Also shown is the pin-out diagram. The IC
is a 74LS138, and is called a *3 to 8-line decoder*. Its function is simply to
convert the eight possible bit patterns on its three input lines (I0, I1 and I2)
to an output (low) on one of its eight outputs. The logic or truth table
shows how inputs are converted to output states by the IC. For instance, if
all three inputs are 0, then output 0 (pin 15) is active (low). Most of the
electronic logic which we will come across has the low state as the active
one – remember this is normally denoted by a bar in the diagrams. Notice
how the decimal value of the input binary number determines which
numbered output goes low. Notice also that this only occurs when the
active high enable on pin 6 is at a 1, and the other enables on pins 4 and 5
are low. If one of these enables is in the wrong state, the outputs remain
high regardless of the inputs.

As an example, Fig. 3.11 shows the address lines A5, A6 and A7
connected (in the correct order) to the inputs, and the IORQ line to its

two active low enables. The active high enable on pin 6 is held permanently high, and so the activation of the 74LS138 depends only upon IORQ being low. The above explanation should make it clear that this circuit can be used to activate a piece of I/O circuitry when the address bus has a given bit pattern, and the IORQ is low as for an IN or OUT statement. If we wish to activate, say, port 31, as above, A5, A6 and A7 will all be low, and when IORQ is also low the output numbered zero (pin 15) will go low. As mentioned above, this only lasts for a very short time, as the MPU passes through that section of program, and it is up to the electronics connected to the 74LS138 to capture the contents of the data bus at that time. However, this is no problem as all the ICs in general use will act many times faster than the MPU.

Figure 3.10 has already shown the type of ouptut IC which might be attached to the decoder of Fig. 3.11. With the address lines shown, each 74LS138 output is selected for just one address on the address bus. The I/O chips attached to these outputs, therefore, can only have one register. If one of them has two registers, Fig. 3.12 shows how to connect it up. There will be an address input on such a chip, perhaps called C/D as shown, which selects control and data registers respectively for 1 and 0. This is connected to A5. The I2 input of the decoder can be permanently held low, and then only the upper half of the table in Fig. 3.11 is active. There will be four decoded outputs for this situation, and each can have one of these chips attached. A5 is connected to the C/D pin of each of the four chips. By using the table in Fig. 3.11, and the fact that A0 to A4 are all 1 for the Spectrum, you can work out the binary patterns on the address bus which will activate these chips, and hence find out their port addresses.

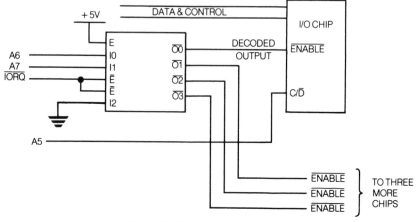

Fig. 3.12. Two-register I/O chip.

To add two PIOs to the Spectrum, each of which occupies four address locations, the 74LS138 would have I2 and I1 connected to ground, and I0 connected to A7. A5 and A6, and the other data and control bus lines would be connected to each PIO as shown in Fig. 3.2. The E-bar pin of one of the PIOs would connect to output zero (pin 15) of the 74LS138, and the other to output one (pin 14).

This gives you some idea of the type of circuit required for general add-ons to your Spectrum, or any other machine. In order to take this aspect of computing further, you will have to learn a certain amount of electronic logic. There are many books on the subject, for many levels of background, from complete novice to engineering level. However, one of the best explanatory and reference books on the subject is Don Lancaster's *TTL Cookbook*, published by Sams. This book will build on the knowledge you have mastered so far, and give you much useful information with which to follow on.

Chapter Four
Robotic Peripherals

Introduction

The first chapter started with a description of the meaning of robotics, and defined some of the aspects of intelligence which robots can have, by referring to the corresponding human qualities. In addition, the robot mouse of the last chapter introduced the basic principles of controlling the mechanics of a robot.

This chapter describes some important interfaces for general robotic use, and aims to provide you with 'cookbook' style information to allow you to design your own systems. The peripherals introduced here would make excellent add-ons to the robot arm of the next chapter, or to the robot mouse of the last chapter.

When using a robot, the more feedback you can use from the surroundings, the better. There are many different sensors available, and some of them give a continuously variable voltage. This chapter shows you how to read these, and use them on a robot.

Movement is the most important output of a robot, and many of the mechanical systems you will see use a special type of motor called a *stepper motor*. An interface for a stepper is given, and you can use it in the design of movable machinery of any kind.

Controlling movement

As we shall see in the next chapter, robot arms are assemblies of jointed mechanical levers, usually with a grasping tool at one end of the assembly, and an unmovable base at the other. The joints are similar to our own arm joints, and arms normally have 4 or 5 degrees of movement, or 'degrees or freedom'. The whole arm can be swung around in a circle on the base, an 'elbow' and a 'wrist' joint can be hinged, and the grasping hand can be rotated through an angle at the wrist. This gives four continuously variable or analogue degrees of freedom. A fifth would be the control of the hand's grasping motion, which may well be controlled simply by an on/off switch, for 'open' and 'close'.

There are several ways to create this movement, and they all at present rely on electromagnetism. This has been introduced in Chapter 1, where the solenoid electromagnet and DC motor were introduced. The rotation of a motor is converted into the movement of a lever or mechanical linkage by gears, belts and pulleys, and the control of this movement depends upon the exact type of motor used. One of the most common, the stepper motor, is described next.

The stepper motor

As you can see, in the above systems accurate rotational movements must be produced. This would be considerably easier if a motor could be found which did not simply spin its shaft continuously when switched on, but rather moved through an accurate and controllable angular step. The motor could be geared into the mechanics as suggested above, but would not theoretically require a feedback control system to stop it when it arrived at its destination. The stepper motor is just such a device, and has been developed to be easily controlled by digital systems.

If you are interested in designing the mechanics of a robot arm yourself, the use of a stepper motor can give you a simple system to control. The following even uses a standard controller chip to make the electronics more straightforward.

There are several types of stepper, and several methods of control. The stepper chosen for description here is the easiest to use, and is called the *four-phase* stepper motor. Figure 4.1 shows a diagrammatic representation of the motor. The exact winding details of the coils may differ from motor to motor, but this shows a possible set-up. The motor consists of three main parts – a pivoted magnet at the centre called the *rotor*, a soft iron *stator* and four coils wound on the stator. The magnetic rotor is rigidly connected to the output shaft which is used to rotate the machinery under control.

To see how the coils are wound, look at coil Cc. This simply winds down the top tongue of the stator, onto the bottom tongue *in the same direction* and out. This means that if a current is passed from C to c, by closing the switch Sc, the two tongues form a couple of electromagnets, aligned in the same direction. This will attract the rotor to turn to line

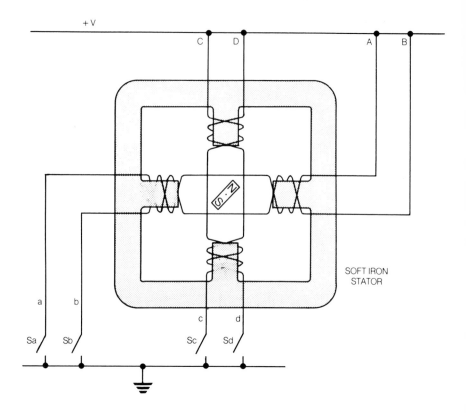

SWITCHES IN ON STATE	Sa & Sc	Sa & Sd	Sb & Sd	Sb & Sc	Sa & Sc
ROTOR POSITION					

Fig. 4.1. The stepper motor.

up with these tongues, with the North pole of the magnet attracted to the top, and the South pole to the bottom. The coil Dd is wound on the same tongues, but in the opposite direction. This means that when it is energised, the rotor will spin around to rest in the opposite direction. Similarly, Aa will cause the rotor's North pole to be attracted to the right, and Bb to the left. By controlling the switches in the four coils, therefore, the rotor can be made to step around at will by as many steps as required. There are limitations, of course, but this shows the principle of how accurate positioning can be achieved.

There are several possible methods of controlling the direction and position of rotation of the rotor, and the table in Fig. 4.1 gives one such sequence for stepping the rotor through four right-angles in a clockwise direction. Notice that in this method two coils are always energised, and the magnet must orientate itself midway between the two magnetic fields produced. In order to reverse the direction of the motor, the sequence is reversed. This gives full control of the mechanics.

The motor illustrated is capable of stepping at angles of 45 degrees per step for more accuracy. This is achieved by adding in steps where the rotor is attracted to the actual tongues of the stator, as well as half way between. This is only a question of adding in steps where only one switch is closed at a time, and is called *half-step mode*. It gives the minimum step angle possible with the motor. Practical motors have more tongues and more magnetic poles on the rotor to reduce the step angle further. A typical commercially available motor will provide a 7.5 degree or even 1.8 degree full step, and half that in half-step mode.

The switches can be closed by hand, or by relays, but neither of these methods is fast enough for robotic control, and one normally replaces the switches with transistors controlled by parallel I/O lines from a computer. The program simply sends the correct pulses for whichever direction is required, and counts the pulses to position the mechanics accurately.

Theoretically, no feedback is required from this control process, as the computer knows exactly how it has controlled the machine in the past. However, it is possible for the motor to slip under conditions of stress, and this would mean that some of the steps may not have occurred. The computer would then have a false idea of its position. It is not uncommon for the robotic elements to have limit switches on them, so that the computer can 'home' the stepper to some known and readable position. This gives the system a datum to work from. In some cases, full feedback of each step is required to ensure that it has occurred in the right sense and degree, and this gives the most accurate type of system.

A stepper project

In order to control the above stepper, you have to build a circuit containing transistor switches, and then control each of the four switches (or phases) individually to achieve the result. A small stepper motor can be controlled using the type of circuit used to switch relays in the previous chapters, but with more powerful transistors. Diodes are needed across the stepper coils as for the relays, but the power required should come from a separate mains power supply, and this will be described later in this chapter. When using steppers, it is a good idea to separate their power supply from that of the logic (but with a common 0 V connection). Also, large capacitors should be used across the supply for smoothing. These precautions help prevent electrical noise from interfering with the processor and electronic logic.

The drawback with this type of control is that a BASIC program may not run fast enough to gain the best from the motor. There is a fair amount to do to make the individual phases perform correctly. If you do wish to use this method of control, you will be able to control the motor more flexibly, but will probably have to learn machine code to achieve the speed. This is highly recommended as an ultimate solution to stepper control, but for a first stab at the subject, the following method of control is easier to set up.

There is a very useful IC on the market called an SAA1027. It takes in three control lines for commands, and includes transistor drivers for direct interfacing to the motor. It will not perform half-step mode, but is an excellent and simple chip to use for a full-step application. The only drawback is that it does not accept TTL control signals. As we shall see, some transistors are required to change the voltage levels of the PIO's TTL signals in order to control this chip.

The following describes an experiment to work a small stepper motor. You should try to buy a stepper which is recommended for use with the SAA1027. Alternatively, ensure that it requires a maximum of 350 milliamps per phase, at about 12 V supply voltage, and has four phases. You will also need to find out which wires do what from the data on the motor.

Figure 4.2 shows the circuit diagram which will be used to interface the stepper to the SAA1027, and this to the PIO. If you cannot find any data on the stepper, you can work out which wires do what by using a multimeter on the resistance range. The coils in the motor are quite low resistance, and you should select the ohms range. There will be five or six wires from the motor. Sometimes, wires A,B,C and D in Fig. 4.2 are all connected together inside the motor, and sometimes they are connected together in pairs as shown, with one wire for C and D, and one for A and B. There are four further wires, labelled a,b,c and d. If the wires are not labelled, you can check the resistance of any two wires. All four coils will have the same resistance, and by checking you will find there are two values of resistance found by the meter. If you have the meter across, say, the wires d and c, you will find double the resistance of, say, d and D. By this means you will be able to identify which wires

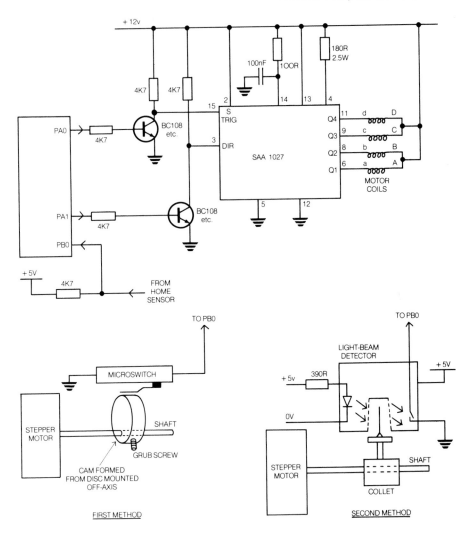

Fig. 4.2. Stepper motor control.

are the four phases, and which are the commons to be connected to +12 V. However, this will not tell you which phase is which. This is found by trial and error. Pick one of the phases to be called d, and there are just three combinations of connection for the other three wires. If you have a 6-wire motor, you will be able to start by choosing both c and d as these will identify the CD wire using the multimeter. This only gives two combinations for the other two wires. You will not damage the motor by this type of trial and error, it will simply not run properly if connected wrongly.

Figure 4.2 shows a circuit for controlling a motor, with feedback from a 'home sensor'. As explained above, if too much stress is put on the motor shaft while it is stepping, it may slip, and some of the steps may be lost. To guard against this possibility, and to allow the motor to be started from a known position, a sensor may be attached to the shaft to identify one given position as the 'home' position. The motor can always be stepped back to the home position by the computer, using a number of steps which it believes to be home, from its memory of the past movement. If this agrees with the actual home position, as identified by the home sensor, there has been no slip. In addition, before stepping begins, it may be useful to be able to start the stepper from a known position so that the computer knows exactly where it is at any time by counting the steps. Use of this home sensor depends upon the actual mechanical application for which the stepper is required.

The PIO is used for the stepper and home sensor interface. The PIO outputs need to be changed to +12 V levels, for the SAA1027, with transistors as shown, and you should use the same type of transistor as in Chapter 2. The SAA1027 and stepper motor are supplied from the same +12 V source. This will be described shortly.

Two methods of constructing a home sensor are shown in Fig. 4.2. The first is a simple microswitch and offset cam on the motor's shaft. A good model shop may have something like this, with a grub screw for fixing to the shaft. Alternatively, buy an ordinary cylindrical collet, and solder a lever to it. As the lever rotates around the shaft axis, the microswitch should be mounted to close and open again, with each revolution, without affecting the motion. Another method of producing a cam is to drill an off-centre hole for the shaft in a disk, and drill and tap a hole to take a small screw for fixing to the shaft. A simple on/off microswitch is all that is needed, and it should be connected to be normally open, and switch 0 V to the signal line into the PIO when home.

A type of home sensor which does not need any contact is also illustrated. You can buy this device complete. It consists of a plastic housing with a slot formed in it. Across the slot an LED shines light onto a light detector. The light detector is connected to some internal switching logic, which holds the signal output high while the light is on. When a lever attached to the shaft enters the slot and breaks the beam, the output signal goes low, and detects the home condition. You can also buy this type of light switch without the internal logic, and it is then up to you to design some electronics to perform the switching.

You may have your own ideas for home sensors, and it is well worth while experimenting to produce the most efficient system.

+12 V power supply

The power supply of the Spectrum is not fitted for controlling mechanical equipment, and as stated above, you should keep it separate anyway to prevent noise problems. Figure 4.3 shows a couple of circuit diagrams for a suitable power supply, which will supply 'raw' or unregulated power for the stepper controller. If you also wish to use it for a +5 V supply, simply connect the +12 V line into the regulator as described in the previous chapters.

The main element of a DC power supply powered from the 240 V mains is the transformer. This is a large iron-cored component with two or more windings formed around it on a 'former'. The object is to change the voltage of the incoming mains to a more manageable and

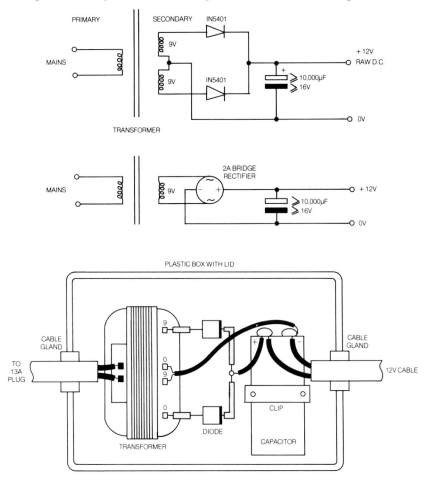

Fig. 4.3. +12 V power supply.

safe working voltage. The principle is that as the AC of the primary changes, it causes magnetic fluctuations in the core, which induce a voltage in the secondary coil(s). The voltage change from primary to secondary depends upon the ratio of coil turns from primary to secondary.

Transformer secondary voltages are usually given as a type of average voltage, called the RMS voltage. For our purposes, 9 V RMS will be sufficient, and the circuits shown will actually produce around 11 V. For this application, you should aim for about 2 A, to allow expansion to two or three motors. If you can buy a transformer with a single 9 V 2 A secondary, then use the second circuit. If you can find one with two 9 V secondaries, which can supply 2 A total, then use the upper circuit. It is worth sticking to around 2 A maximum purely for reasons of space and size – there is no disadvantage to buying one larger, but you should be careful to buy the correct voltage.

In the first diagram, two separate high-current diodes are used, with the two secondaries connected in series. It is important that you connect them end to end as shown in the right way, if they are not already connected in series. The actual direction of winding on the former is important, and if you connect the wrong ends together, you will simply have no output. If they are labelled '0 and 9', connect one of the 9s to the other's 0 to form the centre connection for the 0 V line.

In the second diagram, where only one secondary is used, use a 'bridge' rectifier of at least 2 A capacity, and preferably a little more to be sure. Again, do not use a component which is physically too large if you can help it.

The capacitor shown should be anything from 10000 μF upwards, at a working voltage of 16 V or more. It will almost certainly have screw-fittings for solder tags, and you should try to find the correct tags rather than simply jamming wires into place. Make sure you connect this component the correct way round – you would be quite surprised at the force of explosion which can result otherwise! The same goes for the transformer – make sure you connect the mains to the primary.

The whole supply should be confined to a plastic box, with all internal wires carefully insulated, not with tape, but with proper insulation sleeving. Strip it from some wire if you cannot find the correct material. This is most important, and anyone will tell you that the majority of faults which occur with electronic equipment come from the power supply.

The transformer and capacitor should be bolted down to the base of the plastic box using plastic screws, to prevent any chance of shorts causing high voltages to appear outside the box. A well-fitting plastic lid should be screwed in place for normal use. Both cables should be led into the box through cable glands, which should be the type which can be screwed up by hand to clamp the cable in place. This is one of the most important items in the construction, and should never be missed out. You should use a layout as shown in Fig. 4.3, which separates the low voltage from the mains. Any nuts and bolts which you use to fix the components into the box should be nylon to prevent any chance of mains appearing outside the box at any time.

Finally, remember that mains is dangerous, and that the box should *never* be opened when the mains plug is plugged into a mains socket, even if the socket is switched off. For further safety, a 3 A fuse should be fitted in the mains plug.

Using the stepper

The way in which you use the motor mechanically, and the things you move and control with it, are entirely up to you. The following gives you enough information to be able to use and control it as you wish.

The SAA1027 actually has three inputs, S, TRIG and DIR. S is used to stop the stepper and return it to a given position, but is tied permanently high in this application. However, you can connect S as for the other two control lines, and experiment if you wish. We shall only use the two control lines shown in Fig. 4.2. One of these, TRIG, is the actual step control. It is short for 'trigger'. Each time it receives a rising edge (from 0 to 1), it will step the motor through one step. By this means, a simple train of pulses will set the motor stepping continuously. The other control line is the DIR, or direction control. The level of this line determines the rotational direction of the step action. There are no other controls to worry about, as the SAA1027 takes care of stepping through the correct sequence of phase conditions automatically.

To control the stepper, the PIO must be set up with PA0 and PA1 as outputs, and PB0 as an input. Other combinations of PIO lines could be used, but this gives a situation which is easy to program. The set-up statements are as follows:

```
OUT 95,255
OUT 95,0
OUT 127,255
OUT 127,1
```

The next step would be to send the control lines to a known state by setting them both high using:

```
OUT 31,3
```

The actual direction of the stepper can now be determined, and noted down. To do this, the stepper should be stepped a few times by taking PA0 low and high again repeatedly as a set of pulses. The step occurs as PA0 goes low because the transistor inverts the polarity of the pulse. This is done using:

```
OUT 31,2
```

These statements are chosen to ensure that PA1 remains high, thus leaving the direction constant. Repeating the above statements will step the motor round. If it does not, you have probably connected the motor incorrectly, and you should refer to the above advice on connection.

You should be able to work out for yourself how to change direction, and repeat the process.

To use the home sensor, read in the state of PB0 after each step. If an IN statement gives you a decimal number which is even, you know that the binary equivalent of that number has bit 0 as low. If the number returned is odd, then bit 0 is high. See Appendix 1 if this is not clear. This gives a possible method of checking this bit. The following program starts by setting up the PIO, and then asks for you to input a command. It gives you a choice of 'Home the motor', 'Step forward' or 'Step backwards', and then it asks for the number of steps required. It will also print "HOME" on the screen when the home sensor gives a positive result during a home command. It is assumed that PB0 goes low for the home condition.

```
 10 REM ** SET UP PIO
 20 OUT 95,255: OUT 95,0
 30 OUT 127,255: OUT 127,1
 40 OUT 31,3
 50 REM ** INPUT COMMAND
 60 PRINT "TYPE H FOR HOME"
 70 PRINT "B FOR BACK"
 80 PRINT "AND F FOR FORWD."
 90 PRINT : PRINT
100 INPUT A$
110 IF A$="H" THEN GO TO 400
120 IF A$="B" THEN GO TO 600
```

```
130 IF A$="F" THEN GO TO 800
140 GO TO 100
400 REM ** CHECK IF HOME
410 LET K=IN 63
420 IF 2*INT(K/2)=K THEN PRINT "HOME": GO TO 40
430 REM ** ADVANCE ONE STEP
440 OUT 31,2: OUT 31,3
450 REM ** RETURN TO RECHECK
460 GO TO 400
600 REM ** SET BACKWARD DIR.
610 OUT 31,1
620 PRINT : PRINT
630 INPUT "HOW MANY STEPS? ",A
640 REM ** STEP A TIMES
650 FOR I=1 TO A
660 OUT 31,0: OUT 31,1
670 NEXT I
680 GO TO 40
800 REM ** SET FORWD. DIR.
810 OUT 31,3
820 PRINT : PRINT
830 INPUT "HOW MANY STEPS? ",A
840 REM ** STEP A TIMES
850 FOR I=1 TO A
860 OUT 31,2: OUT 31,3
870 NEXT I
880 GO TO 40
```

The step speeds you will observe with this program are comparatively low, and they cannot be speeded up using BASIC. However, again, many robotic functions are not fast, and the speeds are adequate if the right motor is used for the right mechanical system.

One of the problems with a home sensor is that it may report the condition for a number of nearby step positions. If you are using the sensor, make sure that you make your program aware of the fact that it may take more than one step to clear home. This entirely depends upon the mechanics you have, and you can even adjust the whole system to ensure that there *is* only one home position.

There are many refinements which you can make to this program. For instance, it could be storing the moves you command away to memory, and then repeat the whole sequence whenever you wish. This gives a simple learning example.

The stepper can be used to move a mouse along the floor, position its steering with great accuracy, rotate the hands of a clock, move a hand or arm, and so on. It is a most versatile and useful device, and gives an excellent example of a machine for converting electronic commands into controlled movement.

The next section describes another robotic type interface which allows you to experiment further with attaining human attributes by machine, through speech synthesis.

Speech synthesis

As mentioned in Chapter 1, there are two types of speech synthesis system. The type described here is called *stored speech*, and consists of a speech processor chip (SPC), and a speech ROM containing the data of the words to be spoken. The SPC is intelligent enough to take in a 1-byte word from a PIO, for instance, and perform the complete task of fetching the speech data, and forming the utterance requested. The output is an audio waveform, which requires a certain amount of processing and filtering, and then amplifying. The SPC chip used here is the MM54104 manufactured by National Semiconductor, and you can buy ROMs with standard vocabularies for it, each containing from 50 to 70 words. This chip is extremely easy to use, and gives a representative method of interfacing such systems to the Spectrum. There are other similar speech processors in existence, and most of them interface in a similar manner.

Figure 4.4 shows a block diagram of the speech synthesiser interface, and Fig. 4.5 gives a complete circuit diagram. To build the speech synthesiser project, you will need an SPC, and at least one speech ROM containing a vocabulary of your choice. You can buy these parts from a component supplier, and Fig. 4.5 gives the standard Radio Spares or RS part number of the SPC, which will allow you to track down the IC if all else fails. A catalogue will have to be consulted to choose the speech ROM, as there are several offered, for different vocabularies. You should request the data sheets on both of these ICs. They give the full technical details, and will allow you to take the project further if you wish. The other components specified in the project are straightforward, and freely available.

To explain the working of the system, Fig. 4.4 shows the SPC interfaced to a PIO and some audio circuitry. The word to be spoken is selected by supplying a data bit pattern to the SPC along its word data lines. When the WR line of the SPC rises from 0 to 1, the SPC takes this pattern, consults the speech ROM, and produces the word sounds on

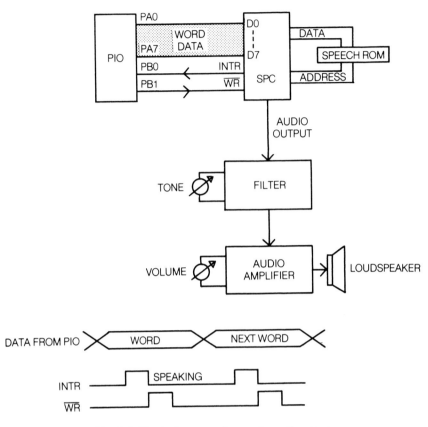

Fig. 4.4. Block diagram of speech synthesiser.

its audio output. To prevent the computer from interrupting this process, there is an output from the SPC which tells the computer that it is busy. This is called INTR (Interrupt). When INTR is 0, the SPC is speaking; INTR rises to a 1 when it has finished. INTR is called a *handshaking* signal, and it provides feedback to the computer to allow the program to process at just the right speed for the best effect. The computer should read this line, and wait until it is high before changing the state of WR again. A diagram shows this process at the bottom of Fig. 4.4. It is meant to illustrate the sequence of events, rather than their exact timing. A word is set up on the data lines by the PIO, INTR is checked, and the computer waits until it is high. The WR line is then taken from low to high, and back, and the SPC starts speaking. INTR goes low to indicate this state. The next word can then be set up on the data lines, and nothing will happen until the computer pulses WR high again. If WR is taken high while the SPC is speaking, it will be interrupted, and will start on the new word which is on the data lines.

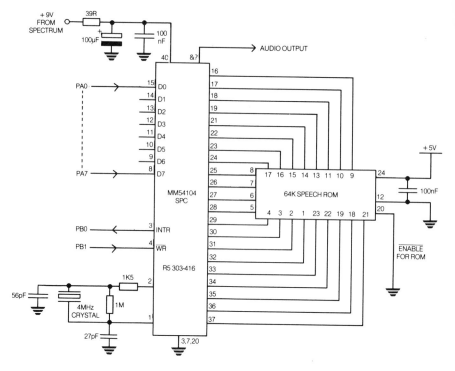

Fig. 4.5. Speech synthesis chip.

For a given word, the SPC derives the details from the speech ROM, and fetches all the necessary data using its data and address buses. It is essential that the ROM is purchased as being specifically compatible with the MM54104 – no other ROM will work. As the data is fetched, the SPC converts it into an audio waveform very near to human speech.

The ROM has an Enable line, pin 20 shown in Fig. 4.5, which will simply be connected to 0 V to enable the ROM continuously. However, if more than one ROM is needed, to increase the vocabulary the ROM Enables could be connected to outputs of the PIO, and the particular ROM required at any time can be enabled by setting its Enable line low. All the other ROMs will be disabled, and will not interfere in any way. The address and data buses of all such ROMs are connected in parallel to the SPC. To further increase the number of ROMs which can be addressed, a 74LS138 can be used to decode three of the six spare PB lines of the PIO into eight enables, as shown in the last chapter. By this means, a total of 16 ROMs could be enabled from all six PB lines of the PIO.

The audio output from the SPC, in Fig. 4.4, gives recognisable speech if amplified, but is produced from a primarily digital source, and contains various frequencies which degrade the intelligibility. The frequencies required are in a band around five or six hundred kilohertz. This is about the frequency of top C on a piano. To improve the quality of the speech, therefore, we need to filter out this band of frequencies, and pass it onto the audio amplifier. This requires an electronic filter which can also incorporate a tone control. The amplifier, with its volume control, is the final link in the chain before the loudspeaker itself.

Electronics of the speech synthesiser

Figure 4.5 shows the connection diagram of the SPC and ROM. As you can see, they literally plug together, and this should be built on a piece of Veroboard, with the two ICs next to each other. The ROM needs +5 V, and the SPC +9 V. The 5 V power supply described in Chapter 2 is sufficient for the ROM. The 9 V comes from the Spectrum PSU via the edge connector, but passes through a simple resistor and capacitor filter to prevent the hum of the 9 V power supply from being heard in the audio. Electronic noise is also removed from the power supply to the ROM by a 100 nF capacitor, which should be placed as near to the ROM as possible.

The SPC also requires a 4 MHz clock, and this is generated by a quartz crystal connected to the SPC as shown. The clock components are freely available, and 4 MHz is a standard frequency of crystal. The capacitors are the usual ceramic discs.

Figure 4.6 shows the audio circuitry. A simple filter using a 741 is illustrated, again fed from the +9 V of the Spectrum, with its own separate filtered power supply. The 741 is the same type as that used for the light detector of the last chapter, but it will perform better as a filter when fed from 9 V rather than 5 V. You can experiment with some of the values shown to gain the best results. The best values to try changing are the 220K resistor and 10 nF capacitor between pins 2 and 6. These two, along with the other 10 nF capacitor, determine the filtered frequencies.

The audio amplifier uses a standard IC called an LM380. The version used here is the 14-pin package. Any other will do, but the pin numbering will have to be changed. This amplifier will give around 1.5 W of output, which will be quite sufficient for normal purposes. More power can be produced from it by increasing the voltage to a maximum of 15 V, when about 2.5 W can be generated.

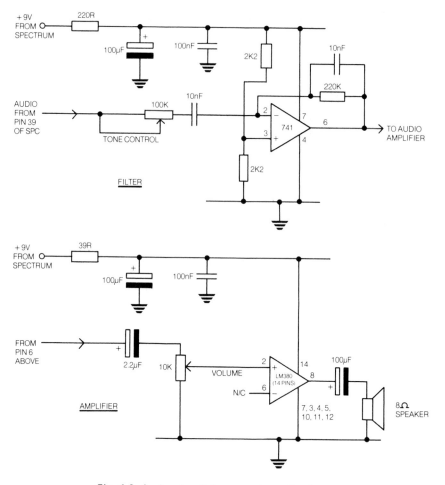

Fig. 4.6. Audio circuit for speech synthesiser.

The capacitors shown in Fig. 4.6 are all ceramic disks unless the electrolytic symbol is used. Make sure you connect the electrolytics the correct way round. In general, use 16 V working devices minimum, but do not use physically large versions, as the layout must be kept as neat as possible. Do not use any very long wires in the audio circuitry, but do not cram the components together into a 'bird's nest'.

If there is a lot of noise and hum on the output, try adjusting the values of the hum-filter components on the 9 V lines. Increasing the capacitor and resistor values will normally help, but do not increase the resistors too much or the voltage will drop significantly to the ICs, and they will work less efficiently.

The quality of audio output from this system is good considering the simplicity of the electronics required. All the words are understandable, and they have a certain amount of natural sounding inflexion. The output can, however, be improved further by using a more sophisticated filter circuit. The technical data on the SPC contains a more complex circuit for you to construct if you are interested.

As an experiment, try bypassing the filter circuit. Take pin 39 of the SPC straight to the positive side of the capacitor on the input of the audio amplifier. This will illustrate the effect of the filter in processing the audio given out by the SPC.

Using the speech synthesiser

Table 3.1 gives the I/O ports for the PIO. Using this information and the connection diagram of Fig. 4.5, the following routine will cause the synthesiser to speak the word in the speech ROM associated with 0 (decimal). For instance, if the 'numbers and letters' ROM has been used, the word 'one' will be spoken.

```
 10 REM *** SET UP PIO A
 20 REM *** AS OUTPUTS
 30 OUT 95,255: OUT 95,0
 40 REM *** SET UP PIO B
 50 REM *** AS PB0 IN, REST OUT
 60 OUT 127,255: OUT 127,1
 70 REM *** SET ALL OUTPUTS ZERO
 80 OUT 31,0: OUT 63,0
 90 REM *** PULSE WR LINE
100 OUT 63,2: OUT 63,0
```

The way in which the PIO is used to set and reset the I/O lines is explained in the last chapter. This routine simply sets all the PA lines to zero, thus selecting the first word in the ROM. Then the WR line connected to PA1 is pulsed high and then low. The rising edge starts the utterance.

The program above does handshake with the SPC using INTR, and this is only necessary for connected phrases. Its main purpose is to allow several words to be spoken without interrupting each other. If it is acceptable for a given application to say the words with a constant delay, there is no need to use the INTR at all. For instance, if the synthesiser is calling out a set of numbers, you can use a PAUSE statement between each word to ensure that there is sufficient delay to prevent interference.

However, as different words will take up different times, a sensible phrase or sentence will need to be spoken with the correct time delays between words, and handshaking is essential. The following program speaks the first ten words in the ROM, using INTR to ensure that there is no overlap, and using PAUSE to achieve a constant gap between words.

```
 10 OUT 95,255: OUT 95,0
 20 OUT 127,255: OUT 127,1
 30 OUT 31,0: OUT 63,0
 40 FOR I = 0 TO 9
 50 REM *** SET UP WORD
 60 OUT 31,I
 70 REM *** START SPEECH
 80 OUT 63,2: OUT 63,0
 90 REM *** CHECK INTR AND
100 REM *** CONT. WHEN HIGH
110 LET K=IN 63
120 IF 2*INT (K/2)=K THEN GO TO 110
140 PAUSE 10
150 NEXT I
```

You should now experiment by writing routines to string words together in an intelligible form.

General robotic applications

Speech synthesis is a very useful addition to a robotic system, giving it personality and greater ability to feed information back to the user. For instance, if a light seeking robot has found a light, it could say so, and then move off towards it informing you of how far it has moved, and whether the light is still being detected. If you add bump switches to the robot, you could program it to inform you when it meets an obstacle. Your program may include a routine to make it bump the obstruction several times, and then attempt to steer around it. If it still meets the obstruction, it would be very useful if it could say so, and perhaps ask for your help. This sort of interaction is at the basis of machine intelligence, and even though it is always possible to use a screen display to inform the user of the state, a better general interaction with the experimenter will come from the use of speech.

An important sense which any robot system will find useful is the ability to monitor levels of a given stimulus. Up to the present point, only digital inputs have been taken in by the computer system. Many stimuli in nature are analogue rather than digital – that is, they vary continuously rather than being simply on or off. Examples of this might be temperature, pressure, the angle of a mechanical lever or arm, and so on. We have already seen one such input, namely light detection, but so far have treated it in a purely digital manner. The light detector simply converted all levels over a certain value to the ON state, and any below to OFF.

In order to input continuous levels of a given parameter, we will first have to convert them to voltage levels. This is done, in the case of light, by an LDR as in Chapter 3. Other physical variables have their own sensors – there are electronic thermometers, for instance, for temperature. Having produced a varying voltage, this must be converted to a digital form for reading by a computer. You will not be surprised to learn that the voltage levels can be converted into 8-bit numbers, and read as binary patterns by eight lines of a PIO. The conversion is called *Analogue to digital conversion*, and there are analogue to digital converts (ADCs) available in IC packages. The next section shows you how to use one of these devices, and suggests how you might couple up a light dependent resistor to monitor varying light levels.

Analogue to digital conversion

Figure 4.7 shows a block diagram of an ADC interface. An LDR, labelled R2, changes its resistance according to the incident light level. The more light, the lower the resistance. This produces varying input voltages to the ADC. This continuously variable voltage is compared with a reference voltage by the ADC, and a binary number generated depending upon the difference between the input and the reference voltages. The PIO reads this binary number, and the computer program can thus 'see' the changing light levels in the surroundings.

If the binary number produced has eight bits, then the ADC gives 255 (decimal) when the ADC input voltage equals the reference voltage, and gives 0 (decimal) when the input voltage is 0 V. This gives the maximum voltage swing of the device, and it is up to the electronics feeding the ADC with the variable voltage to ensure that this voltage remains within these bounds. For instance, if the reference voltage is +5 V, then a continuous voltage swing from 0 V to +5 V will result in all the numbers from 0 to 255 being produced. This effectively splits the 5 V swing into 256 equal voltage levels, each one being:

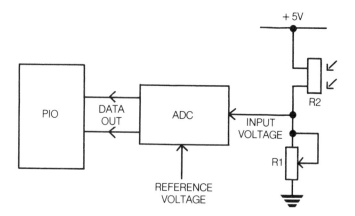

Fig. 4.7. Analogue to digital conversion.

$$\frac{1}{256} \times 5 \text{ V} = 0.0195 \text{ V}$$

You will note that small variations of voltage may not be noticed by the ADC, because unless the present voltage is just on the edge of one of these voltage levels, the voltage may have to change by 0.0195 V actually to cause the binary number to change. The voltage difference (0.0195 V, here) between adjacent voltage levels determines the resolution or accuracy of the ADC. ADC theory is quite complex, and we will leave it here. The following gives a practical use of an ADC.

The LDR in Fig. 4.7 has a resistance which can vary from hundreds of kilohms to a few tens of ohms as the light level changes. This makes it difficult to choose R1, and you will have to experiment to find the best value for your application. However, if you use a variable resistor of around 10K for R1, this gives a fairly broad variation of voltages for average lighting conditions.

An ADC example

Figure 4.8 shows an example of an ADC circuit, and has a number of additions to the simple case in Fig. 4.7. The IC converter used is the ZN427, which is freely available, has one analogue input channel, and converts this voltage to eight bits of data. It has an internal voltage reference of 2.5 V, which is available on pin 8. This is fed back into the ADC on pin 7 to give the ADC its reference voltage against which to compare the input analogue voltage on pin 6. To ensure that this reference remains smooth and unchanging, a 1 MFD capacitor is

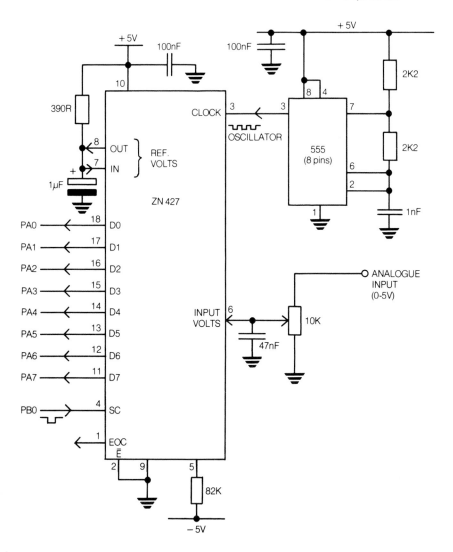

Fig. 4.8. Analogue to digital converter (ADC).

connected to the reference voltage as shown. The 390 Ω resistor is an external part of the ADC's voltage reference circuit. Also, notice that there is a 100 nF capacitor from the +5 V on pin 10 to ground, to smooth out any electronic noise on the power supply.

The ZN427 needs a −5 V supply, and this is taken through an 82K resistor to the ADC's pin 5 from the Spectrum edge connector. The binary number output is fed directly to eight bits of the PIO for reading by the computer program.

A further bit is required from the PIO to command the ADC to perform the conversion; this is called the *start conversion* line (SC), and is on pin 4 of the ZN427. It is then shown coming from PB0 of the PIO in this case, which is set as an output. When SC is pulsed low by the PIO, as shown, the ZN427 takes in the analogue voltage, compares it with the reference voltage, produces the binary number on its output, and then signals that this process is complete by taking its EOC (*end of conversion*) line (pin 1) high. This can be used for handshaking if required. The binary number output is remembered on the data out lines until the next falling edge on SC changes it to the next value. In fact, the data out lines can be tri-state just as the PIO data lines, but in this circuit the E-bar line (pin 2) which controls this is tied low to enable the data out lines continuously.

The process of conversion is sequential, and as such needs an oscillating clock to time its activities. It is provided by an 8-pin IC called a 555, which is universally available, and is used for a number of clock and timing purposes. It is chosen here purely as a simple and economical method of producing the required clock. Any oscillator would do, but the frequency must not exceed 900 kHz. The 555 circuit shown is calculated to give around 200 kHz which is many times faster than the BASIC program governing the use of the circuit can act. After the SC falls from high to low, it takes about 45 μs to perform the conversion, with this clock. It is only necessary to monitor EOC, to see when this process is complete, if your program acts so fast that there is a danger of its sending another SC falling edge before the conversion is complete. This is not the case here, and EOC will be disregarded.

Note that the 555 IC has a 100 nF capacitor on its supply line, to prevent it from transmitting noise to other devices. This ceramic disk should be mounted as near to the 555 as possible, and with the shortest possible leads.

The analogue input shown here varies from 0 V to +5 V, and needs to be reduced to swing from 0 V to 2.5 V, as this is the ADC's reference voltage. The 10K variable resistor allows this to be achieved when set to its mid point, and will allow the circuit to be tested. Note that a 47 nF ceramic disk capacitor is connected from the analogue input of the ADC (pin 6) to ground. This helps to prevent fast-changing voltage spikes from reaching the ADC, and upsetting its readings.

This system gives a potential accuracy of 1 in 256, or around 0.4%. This is more than we require here, and if we were simply to leave the least significant bit (LSB) from pin 18 unconnected, we should still be able to read the voltage to better than 1%. This suggests a very economical method of using just one side of the PIO, instead of having to use eight bits of one side for the data, and an extra bit from the other side for SC.

Figure 4.9 shows this interface suggestion in outline, and all the other connections are as in Fig. 4.8. The LDR is also shown connected to a 10K variable resistor to allow some adjustment to be made for different lighting conditions. This circuit will be assumed in the following.

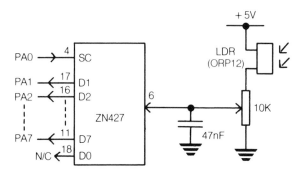

Fig. 4.9. Application for the ADC.

The whole circuit should be constructed on Veroboard as normal, and powered by the PSU described in Chapter 2. The ZX PSU's 9 V supply has enough capacity for this project. Before pushing the IC's into their sockets, power up and check that the Spectrum resets correctly, and that the correct voltage levels, including the negative supply, appear at the correct socket pins. It is also a good idea to check that the voltage at pin 6 of the ZN427's socket varies as light is varied to the LDR, and that the voltage does not exceed 2.5 V at that point. Adjust the variable resistor if necessary. Having made these checks, switch off and plug in the ICs. Check the above again, taking care not to short any IC pins together as you probe around with your meter. If you need to check that the 555 is working, you will need some further test gear. A logic probe is quite sufficient for this purpose.

If all is well, you can check out the operation of the ADC using the programming hints given in the next section. This will allow you to use the circuit for many types of analogue feedback from your robot devices.

If you need more than one ADC channel for several analogue voltages, you can attach another ZN427 to the other side of the PIO, and then two more to another PIO if you wish. Also, they will all run from the same 555 clock. However, the better course is to use the experience gained from this simple example, and the interfacing advice in this book, to use a multi-channel ADC. There are several on the market, and you should ask a component supplier which ones they stock, and obtain manufacturer's data on them. You will find that some of them interface in a similar way to a general I/O chip such as a PIO.

Do not buy any chips until you are sure you can interface them, unless you find a suitable circuit in a magazine or book. In any case, you are always recommended to read the data on any chip you use, including the ZN427 used here.

It is worth pointing out here that some ZN427 data is a little confusing as to the exact order of the data lines. They are sometimes labelled the other way round, with D0 labelled as bit 8, and D7 labelled as bit 1. As long as you stick to the pin connections given here, your circuits will work correctly.

Using the ADC

The following assumes that the PIO is interfaced as previously, and that the ZN427 connects as in Fig. 4.9.

To check the ADC out, turn the 10K variable resistor's wiper to the mid-point position, and type in the following program:

```
 10 REM *** SET UP PIO A-SIDE
 20 REM *** PA0 TO OUT, REST IN
 30 OUT 95,255: OUT 95,254
 40 REM *** SET SC HIGH
 50 OUT 31,1
 60 REM *** PRINT 40 READS OF ADC
 70 FOR I=1 TO 40
 80 REM *** PULSE SC LOW THEN HIGH
 90 OUT 31,0: OUT 31,1
100 REM *** PRINT VALUES IN COLUMNS
110 PRINT IN 31,
120 NEXT I
130 REM *** CLEAR SCREEN AND REPEAT
140 CLS : GO TO 30
```

This program simply reads the data from the ADC, and presents the numbers it finds in two columns on the screen in a continuous loop. It starts by setting the PIO A-Side so that PA0, which is connected to SC, is an output, and the rest are inputs. Only seven of the available bits are used, and this is accurate enough for the present purposes. The SC line is then pulsed to command the ADC to perform the conversion, and by the time the program comes around to performing the IN statement in line 110, the conversion has been complete for some time.

As you vary the light to the LDR, the numbers displayed by this program will also vary – the more light, the higher the number. The numbers will only be odd numbers from 1 to 255, as the IN statement always reads a 1 in the LSB from PA0. This is simply due to the fact that a 1 is left on this output line by the program in line 90, and the PIO always reads back the last state set on an output.

This program allows you to check the circuit, and adjust the variable resistor for the best effect. Different lighting conditions will require different settings. Do not be afraid to change the 10K variable resistor for other values for experimentation. You will find that the LDR is a fairly sensitive device, and useable over a wide range of lighting conditions.

The numbers do not react instantly to changing light levels, and you may have to read the value several times before it settles down. Also, the number will often flip between two nearby values, depending upon the exact value of the input voltage. Other variations come from noise along the power lines, and noise into the voltage input of the ADC. The capacitors mentioned above absorb some of this variation, but you should change these values, and experiment with different layouts to gain the best effect. In any case, it is always worth looking for a range of voltage levels rather than a specific number when using an ADC. It is also worth reading the number several times and comparing one reading with another until you are satisfied that the ADC has settled down.

Applications

The first application for a device such as this could be on the robot mouse. Instead of using a single threshold level to switch an electronic switch, your controlling program could perform different actions depending upon various ranges of ambient light level. For instance, a light seeking robot could be programmed to look for a low level of light at first, and steer towards a light source by detecting the increasing level of light. When the light source is reached, the robot could notice that the level has reached maximum, and steer around through 180 degrees to start looking for another source.

Other variables could be monitored. For instance, battery state could be checked continuously, and when low the robot could seek out a particular source of light, say one coloured in a particular way, and detected by a special LDR with a filter. The robot could steer towards this 'home' position, and automatically slide into a special port containing contacts for recharging the batteries.

The list of intelligent activities you can perform is infinite. The whole of machine intelligence takes on a new dimension when used to control a mechanical device with sensors and servos which can carry out commands, and check on these actions and the outside world continuously. This is exactly how the human body works, and forms the basis for all our hopes for the future of robotics.

The next chapter describes a class of robots which can act in a similar manner to a human arm. You can design and build your own mechanics, but this is beyond the scope of this book, so some standard robot arms which you can buy are described.

Chapter Five
Robot Arms

Introduction

Robotics is a young subject, and much of modern robotics is concerned with general movement and the control of human-like robot arms. The robot mouse of Chapter 3 gave an example of a simple system to investigate intelligent locomotion, and this chapter is devoted to describing robot arms. It is aimed at giving you a flavour of the types of low cost mechanical device which you can buy and control. The only way you will be able fully to appreciate the control of robot arms is to try one out for yourself. All the arms mentioned below come with a manual, which explains how to use the device.

Another alternative is to use the stepper motor interface described in the last chapter, design your own mechanical arm and interface it to the Spectrum. This requires a reasonable amount of mechanical skill, and a good supply of cogs, gears, mechanical tools and so on. The stepper motors are fairly freely available, and the other electronics should give you little trouble. However, if you do not feel sufficiently well versed in the mechanical construction, but wish to experiment with a robot arm, the best plan is to buy one of the standard units available, and interface it to your Spectrum. This chapter starts by describing one of the lowest cost robot arms on the market, with an interface to the Spectrum.

As you read through this chapter, bear in mind the principles and interfaces described in the book so far. As a robot arm is being controlled, it would be interesting to add both light detection at the end of the arm, and speech to inform the user of the state of the system at any time. By this means, the system becomes more and more of a true robot emulating human function.

Later sections examine some other robot arms to show you typical devices on the market. Robotics is a rapidly expanding field, and the arms chosen are sufficiently general to ensure that new devices will still be familiar to you when the present ones are understood.

Appendix 4 gives the address of each of the companies mentioned below, and you are advised to contact them for latest price and availability.

Servo motors and steppers

The majority of robot arms which you will meet are controlled and actuated by *stepper motors*. Steppers are a natural computer peripheral, as they are digital devices, and provide accurate repeatable results. However, systems using steppers are expensive. For this reason, the first arm described in this chapter is a low cost machine which works by controlling DC motors using an internal feedback system to check continuously on their position. The arm's movement is not as accurate or repeatable as the stepper motor controlled arms introduced later, but it is one of the cheapest methods of starting in robotics, and excellent for experimentation.

The general principle of control used in the arm to be described is that of the *servo motor*. This is based around an ordinary DC motor, such as might be found in a model train set, for instance. Its output shaft is geared down to operate the levers of the robot. If a battery is connected across such a motor, it simply spins its shaft until the battery power is removed. For robotic control, it is necessary to check upon the angle through which the shaft has rotated using some sort of feedback device. When the feedback device informs the controller that the motor has rotated sufficiently to move the arm to the desired position, battery power is removed, and the arm comes to rest. There are many types of feedback device for this application, and Fig. 5.1 shows one of them.

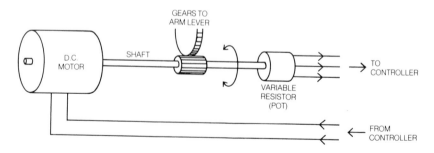

Fig. 5.1. The servo motor.

The shaft of the motor is shown rigidly connected to that of a variable resistor or 'potentiometer' (pot). As the shaft turns, it varies the position of the potentiometer's wiper. If the shaft has to rotate through several turns, a special 'multiturn' pot is used.

The controller is responsible for switching the motor on, and monitoring the resistance of the pot. When it reaches the correct value, the motor is switched off. This allows the controller to know the exact position of the attached arm lever at any time. The controller effectively converts any instruction it receives to move the lever to a given position, into a required value of resistance. It then switches on the motor, in the correct direction, until the required resistance is reached.

The way in which such a controller works is beyond the scope of this book, and the arm described performs this controlling function using some special electronic circuits of which the computer user is not aware. We say that this control is 'transparent' to the user. All the computer will have to do is to send bit patterns to an output port, and the robot arm's electronics will control the required movement.

The Micro Grasp robot arm

The Powertran Micro Grasp is a complete robot arm available in kit form, and configured to attach to a Sinclair ZX81. This section describes the arm, shows you how to connect it to a Spectrum, and suggests some of the control you can exercise with this splendid little peripheral.

Figure 5.2 shows a sketch of the arm, which stands on a base, and has a gripper at the end to grasp objects. The base holds the power supply unit, which requires a 220–240 V mains input at 100 mA, and produces all the power supplies required by the arm. The power supply components also provide ballast for stability, and being confined to the base they safely keep the mains away from any external parts of the arm and its electronics. The arm weighs 8.6 kg, can hold 0.45 kg with the arm at its fullest extension, and has a gripper force of 0.9 kg. The payload of even quite large personal robot arms is never very great, and it is only in the industrial area that arms are found which can pick up more than a few kilograms.

The arm's reach is 290 mm, and has an operating volume which is within part of a sphere of radius 250 mm. There are four rotational axes, and each can be controlled to an angular accuracy of 1 in 256. The repeatability of movement of the arm, measured at the gripper, is to an accuracy of ±6 mm. The gripper can be moved by the arm at a speed of up to 125 mm/s.

The base holds a motor to rotate the arm about a vertical axis; this is

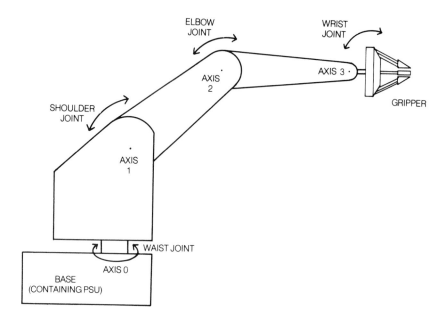

Fig. 5.2. Sketch of the Micro Grasp.

called the *waist* joint. Also in this base is the feedback pot to ensure that the controller rotates the waist to the correct angular position commanded by the computer. This axis of movement is called axis 0, and has about 170 degrees of movement from one end of its travel to the other.

Axis 1 is the *shoulder* joint, and has about 105 degrees of movement. Axis 2 is the *elbow* joint, and axis 3 the *wrist* joint; each has about 160 degrees of movement. All of these joints have their motors and feedback pots mounted at the joints themselves, and the motors drive through gearboxes. The robots described in the later sections have motors mounted near the base, and transmit the actuation through belts and pulleys to the joints. This is the more general design, and the Micro Grasp is unusual in this respect.

The final control is the gripper movement, which is either open or closed, with nothing in between. This is actually controlled by a fifth motor which rotates a lead-screw into a thread to pull the grippers closed, or release them open. Theoretically, this motor could also be controlled to give in-between positions for the gripper, but it does not have a feedback pot, and hence is not controlled in this way by the standard system.

By controlling the degree and direction of the motors, the gripper can be taken to any point in some three-dimensional volume around the base of the machine. Moving from one point to another is generally relatively easy. However, planning the movement so that the gripper follows some predefined curve, or a straight line, is a very interesting and challenging problem.

Imagine, for instance, that the arm is extended straight out horizontally from the base, and you wish to move the gripper to touch some point near to the base. Figure 5.3 suggests how it might be done. You could estimate the angles A, B and C, and simply command the joints to move to those angles. However, suppose that we wanted the end of the gripper to traverse the distance in a straight line from X to Y. It is necessary to move each joint a little at a time rather than simply moving them separately and sequentially through the required angles. Ideally, the joints should all be moving at the same time. This is

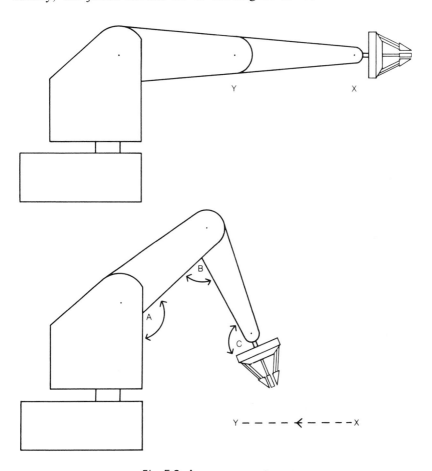

Fig. 5.3. Arm movement.

perfectly possible, and is only a matter of sending the correct commands to the controller.

Controlling a robot arm is a question of a great deal of practice, and the above exercise is an excellent one for learning the types of movement needed to control the actual path of the robot's movement. An extension of this is to try to write some programs to command the robot to write letters and words using a felt-tip pen on paper. As you learn to control the unit, you will naturally find the best place in the robot's volume of movement to place the paper, and the easiest letters to write. This could be the start of an interesting project to teach the robot to first write its name, and then use a speech synthesiser to speak the individual letters, or even string them together phonetically, and speak the words correctly, with the right synthesiser.

Other important tasks which an arm should be capable of performing include picking objects up, and moving them from one place to another. This could be done at first without worrying about the actual path the object takes, or the orientation of the object. The next step is to be able to carry a glass of water without spilling it. This could be done by picking the glass up and carrying it very close to the ground for a short distance, controlling the minimum number of degrees of freedom. The next step would be to control the wrist at the same time, as we do, to keep the glass upright no matter what orientation the rest of the arm takes. Comparing these efforts with the way our arm does the same thing with such ease, you will quickly see how complex the matter of controlling even simple human actions can be. You will find that it is always useful to watch a human arm perform the actions you are trying out with the robot arm, and use this as a clue to the way in which the joints must be moved.

Once you have a robotic set-up, the experimental areas you can try are endless, and you will find yourself inventing new ideas continuously.

Electronic interface to the Spectrum

The Micro Grasp does not need an I/O chip for interfacing, and can be connected onto the Spectrum's buses directly. If an I/O chip is used, its output lines will have to emulate the IORQ, WR, address and data lines to act exactly as described below. This can be done, and though it requires more interfacing electronics than the method described here, it has the advantage that several robotic devices can be used at once by interfacing more than one PIO to the Spectrum at the same time.

The Universal Computer Interface supplied with the Micro Grasp is fitted out to plug straight into a ZX81, and requires a little modification to work on the Spectrum. Firstly, on the ZX81 the interface occupies memory space as opposed to I/O, and this requires MREQ instead of IORQ, along with most of the address bus lines of the MPU to be fed to the interface. All the memory addressing capability of the MPU is used up in the Spectrum, as we saw in Chapter 1, and we will use I/O ports as for the previous projects in this book.

Figure 5.4 shows how to connect up the Spectrum edge connector. The line labelled MREQ on the Micro Grasp board will connect to IORQ on the Spectrum. A2, A1, A0 and WR on the Micro Grasp will connect to A7, A6, A5 and WR, respectively, on the Spectrum. The data bus connects straight through as shown, and there must be a common 0 V line against which all the logic levels are referenced.

In addition to the above connections, the Micro Grasp has a section of address decoding on its board which must be deactivated before the above connections will work. This is achieved by leaving IC2 out, and connecting the solder pads of its pin 13 to +5 V, at pin 24. This is shown in Fig. 5.4.

If you decide to connect the Micro Grasp to your Spectrum, you should purchase the correct PCB edge connector for the controller board, and solder your connection wires to this. Do not solder wires directly to the board, as this will do it no good, and make it hard to disconnect the board at a later date. Also, as usual, do not use long wires from the Spectrum to any external circuitry, as it loads the buses and can stop the computer from working. You should take all the precautions suggested for the PIO interface construction in the last chapter, and switch off immediately if anything strange happens, and inspect all the circuitry with great care before continuing.

Commanding the robot

With the connections made as above, the degrees of freedom of the robot are controlled by sending 8-bit numbers to the I/O addresses associated with the various functions. These numbers vary from 0 to 255, and are equivalent to the angles to which each axis is to move. For instance, if the I/O port for axis 0 were sent the number 128, then the whole arm would swing around to the mid position on its base. Lower numbers would swing it one way, and higher the other. The four axes are all commanded in this manner, but the gripper has a simpler control function. There are two I/O ports for the gripper, one for the command

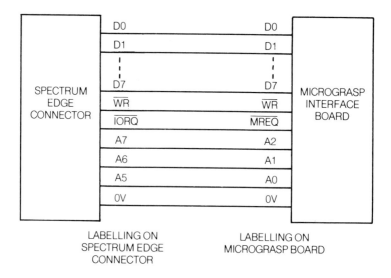

LABELLING ON
SPECTRUM EDGE
CONNECTOR

LABELLING ON
MICROGRASP BOARD

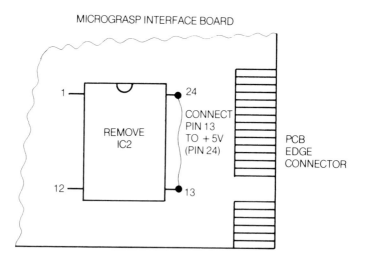

Fig. 5.4. Spectrum interface.

'open', and the other for 'close'. Any OUT statement to the 'open' port will open the gripper, while an OUT to the other will close it. The actual data sent is irrelevant. The electronics of this control are taken care of by the Micro Grasp's interface board. As you can see, six I/O ports are required, and the three address bus lines sent to the interface give eight, leaving two spare.

Table 5.1 defines the actions of the I/O ports on the Micro Grasp, given the connections as in Fig. 5.4. Remember that A0–A4 are all 1.

Table 5.1. Micro Grasp functions.

I/O port	A7	A6	A5	Axis contacted
31	0	0	0	Axis 0 waist joint
63	0	0	1	Axis 1 shoulder joint
95	0	1	0	Axis 2 elbow joint
127	0	1	1	Axis 3 wrist joint
159	1	0	0	Unused
191	1	0	1	Gripper close
223	1	1	0	Gripper open
255	1	1	1	Unused

Thus if you type in OUT 31,0, the Micro Grasp's waist joint will swing round fully one way. OUT 223,0 will open the gripper, as will OUT 223,45 or any other value sent to that I/O port. The interface board only uses the fact that this port has been contacted, and not the actual data sent to it.

As you can see, controlling the robot is straightforward, and any task which the arm can physically perform should be able to be programmed. As indicated above, while it is comparatively easy to command the arm to move from one place to another, it is difficult to make it follow a given path.

An interesting problem is to make the system learn a series of tasks. You will need a program which allows you to drive the arm around at will from the keyboard. Once this is achieved, you will have to add a supplementary routine to remember each action as you perform it. The operations can then be sent to the robot one by one, at a sensible speed, to make it repeat the sequence.

As you experiment with more and more intelligent functions, you will find that they become quite memory intensive, and the larger memory version of the Spectrum is a great advantage.

The Armdroid

A more expensive, but more accurate robot arm is the Colne Robotics Armdroid. This is shown in Fig. 5.5. Here you see that the axes are similar to the Micro Grasp, but that the motors are mounted around the base of the machine. There are six motors, and they are all steppers using 'open loop' control, i.e. there is no feedback, and it is up to the control software to keep track of how many steps have been taken on each motor. There is an optional extra set of home switches which act as described in Chapter 4.

As Fig. 5.5 shows, there is a great similarity between this robot and the last one described. There is more sophistication and accuracy in this case, but the device costs twice as much. Five angles of movement are shown in the diagram, and this includes rotation of the gripper with a

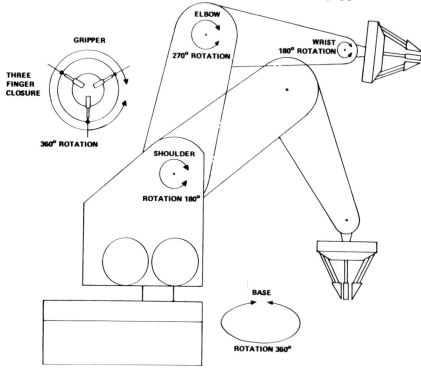

Fig. 5.5. Armdroid (reproduced by courtesy of Colne Robotics Co Ltd).

full 360 degree of freedom. In addition, the gripper is continuously controllable by one of the motors. This gives a very flexible system, and as the motors are not mounted on the arm, the assembly is fairly light, and the centre of gravity quite low for stability. The base houses the motors' controller, and the mains power pack is separate.

Each motor drives a spindle, and a belt pulley. The belt then drives a further pulley and cable in order to transmit the rotational motion to gears at the various joints. The gearing is light but firm, and must be adjusted to ensure that the steppers do not slip and miss steps. If the home sensors are used, the software could check every so often and correct any slip which may have occurred. To do this, the program would have to send the motor to a home position, and note whether the home sensor was activated. The system could count the number of steps needed to correct, and hence signal the user as to the amount of slip, and in which joints. This gives the robot the ability to self-diagnose any failure.

The arm can reach out to 430 mm from the base, and has a positional accuracy of 4 mm. The weight of the robot, not including power supply, is just 3.5 kg, with a payload capacity of 0.3 kg at full extension. The gripper force is about 2 kg. The robot is well adapted to fine control and manipulation, but cannot handle heavy loads.

Electronic interface

There is a standard interface available for the Spectrum, along with software to drive it.

The actual interface is via an 8-bit I/O port. Three bits of this are used to select one of the six motors, and four bits are used actually to drive the four phases of the selected stepper motor. The eighth bit is used to signal data direction. When this bit is low, data may be written to the motors, and when high the home sensors can be read.

The Armdroid has an electronic stepper interface board which converts the digital stepper phase lines into current drive for the motor. The software has to switch the phases correctly to make the stepper step. This would be an excellent application for using the SAA1027 to save the software from having to perform this task.

The Spectrum interface consists of a board which plugs into the Spectrum edge connector, and interfaces to the 8-bit port on the Armdroid controller board. Enough software is supplied on cassette to allow you to experiment with the arm, and the software listing is available to allow you to understand how the programs work, and use them to write your own.

Interfacing the Armdroid to the Spectrum is thus merely a question of plugging in and switching on.

Cyber 310

Figure 5.6 shows an arm called the Cyber 310. It is controlled in a similar manner to the last example, but has no interface for a Spectrum at present. It is controlled by an 8-bit parallel port, called a 'Centronics' port. This simply contains eight data lines, a 'busy' line and a 'strobe' line. Data is sent to the port, and handshaking is performed in a similar

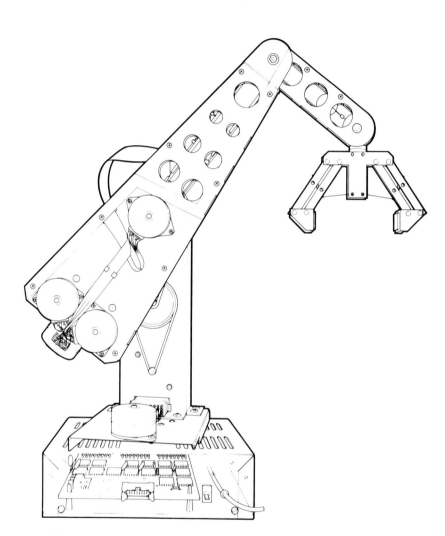

Fig. 5.6. Cyber 310 (reproduced by courtesy of Cyber Robotics Ltd).

manner to that of the speech synthesiser of Chapter 4. There the INTR line was similar to 'busy', and WR similar to 'strobe'. By this means, motors are selected, and the stepper motor phases controlled through the usual current drivers. This requires a good deal of software, and should really be controlled by machine code as BASIC is rather slow for actual stepper phase control. Another solution is to use the SAA1027 as suggested in the last section. This would allow fairly fast full-step mode steps to be performed from BASIC.

This arm has some of the motors mounted half way up the side, as shown. Most of the drive is transmitted by belt and stainless steel cable, and the arm is able to move in a highly flexible manner due to its particular construction. It has six degrees of freedom as for Armdroid, but is generally able to move through greater angles. The resolution of its movement is 0.9–1.5 mm, which is highly accurate, and when fully extended its upper arm measures 820 mm from base to gripper tip. Its maximum payload is 0.25 kg, and it weighs 15 kg.

Conclusion

The arms described above have been chosen to show the low cost end of the robot arm market. Specific prices cannot be given here due to the continuous revision which manufacturers make to their pricing. However, you should expect to pay between £250 and £750 for a robot arm. Greater accuracy and flexibility is provided with greater cost. There are several arms on the market in this area, and the best plan is to purchase one of the many computing or robotic magazines which adorn the shelves of any newsagent. This will also give you further information on new devices continually coming on to the market, with reviews and adverts to keep you up to date.

As mentioned previously, the alternative is to design and build your own arm from scratch. This is by no means impossible, and you could start by making just one axis work, gain some experience with its control, and build upon this basis. A good model shop will be able to sell you a large range of cogs and gears, and you can cut aluminium sheet for the sides of the arm. Study the mechanics of as many robot arms as you can before starting, and gain as many hints as possible from these.

One of the drawbacks of most of the arms on the market is that they provide very little in the way of feedback senses. This book has suggested some which you might consider adding to a robot arm to make it more intelligent.

It is worth building up experience in as many robotic senses and controls as possible, as this will allow you to build more and more human-like machines, with a greater and greater ability to display intelligence.

Appendix One
Binary, Hexadecimal and the ASCII Code

Introduction

The Spectrum manual introduces some of the concepts given in this appendix, but only from the programming point of view. This appendix explains these ideas to allow you to understand the electronics of the machines. The most important idea describes how a computer stores, and hence communicates, data electronically. The ideas are described from that point of view.

You should become familiar with the entire Spectrum manual before reading this appendix.

Computer storage of numbers

You may already know most of the things needed to understand the computer's internal electronic language from your programming. For instance, you may already understand binary numbers. Let us first of all see how computers use this type of system, and why. We will do this by considering a simple type of memory.

A finger-operated toggle switch is the simplest form of memory device. It has two states – 'on' and 'off'. Such a simple switch has no more possible states, and it would be of little use to have less! When the switch is on, this state is 'remembered' until someone turns it off. This is the essence of all computer memory, and even though the concepts involved can become extremely complex, if you remember this fact you will always be able to understand memory devices.

Now suppose that you arrange a set of toggle switches to allow you to set up a bank of lights, one per switch. How many different states can this bank of lights take? This depends, of course, upon the number of switches. If there is just one, there will only be two states, as above (on and off). If there are two switches, you will be able to produce four different light states. These are: both on, both off, and two ways around for one on and one off. It is no coincidence that the number of states (four) is the square of two, i.e. four = two × two. In fact, you can take this further. If there are three lights, you will be able to produce 2 × 2 × 2 = 8 states (2 to the power of 3), and so on. This should show you that for eight lights, there are 2 to the power of 8, or 256, different combinations possible.

This idea of doubling up, depending upon the number of switches, is fundamental to digital computing.

Computer storage of characters

As we all know, one of the main qualities of a computer is that it has memory. It is not enough simply to be a very clever calculator, it is essential to all computing tasks that there is a lot of memory available to store data, variables, letters, numbers, text of any type, etc. Consider for a minute how this memory should be implemented. Could we simply produce electronic devices (perhaps multi-way switches) each with enough states to be able to store any number, letter, abbreviation mark, special symbol, etc, etc? When we wish to store a letter from a friend, we could simply store each character in its own switch, and then read the state of each switch back to recreate the letter.

For a number of reasons, the decision was made many years ago to stick to simple 'two-state' devices, i.e. on/off switches. If you have done some programming, you will already know how quite complex data can be stored by these simple devices. There is an internationally agreed code, called the ASCII code (American Standard Code for Information Interchange). This code is based around a group of seven switches, and each switch may be on or off. This gives just 128 different combinations (2 raised to power 7), and each possible combination is attached to a symbol – a letter, number or special character. On the Spectrum, however, this list of characters is extended to twice this size, and you should already be familiar with the very rich variety of different symbols, some of which you can even define yourself, which are available. The Spectrum manual gives a complete list of the codes, and gives a number of very useful programs which you can try out to practise using them. To be able to represent any one of these 256 different codes, you will need eight bits in the code, as you can see by using the Spectrum.

Imagine a memory bank composed of rows and rows of (on/off) switches. Each row has eight switches, and may thus represent, via the character code, one of 256 different characters which a human would recognise in a piece of text (i.e. letters, numbers, graphics, etc). If there were enough rows, you could hold the whole of the works of Shakespeare, character by character, in this memory bank. There is thus no limit, other than practical, to the resources of such memory.

Computerised calculations, and number bases

There are other things which one would want to store in this bank – calculations for instance. A computer system which could not calculate would be rather restricted. This implies that we ought to be able to store numbers, other than just as a coded symbol – the digits 0 to 9 are symbols in the ASCII code just like the letters, etc. It is necessary to store the numbers in a manner which allows us to *calculate* with them. To see the distinction, imagine calculating with numbers represented in the Roman numbering system. That system is a code which is perfectly capable, like the ASCII code, of representing and storing any number, but just try long division with it if you have a few days to spare!

It is very important to store your numbers in a manner which is consistent with calculative processes. This means storing (or representing) them logically according to some standard 'base', as follows.

We have ten fingers, much to our detriment in the world of computers, and we 'count to base ten' (called the *denary* system). That is, we start at zero, and go up to 9 before switching to a new column and counting up to 99. Then we switch to a new column to count from 100 (ten squared) up to 999. Then comes 1000 (ten cubed, or ten multiplied by itself three times). And so on. Notice how any number, no matter how large or small, can be represented by combinations of the ten digits (0–9) – the same number as the base. Any other base could have been chosen, and if you restrict yourself to using just two digits, say 0 and 1, then you will be counting to the base 2, called *binary*. You may already be familiar with this if you have used your Spectrum in this form, but the following table (which is the same as in the Spectrum manual) shows you how this is done. (Hexadecimal is explained below.)

Notice how each time that a power of 2 is reached (i.e. 2,4,8,16), a new column has to be started, just as for the powers of ten in the decimal number system. You should study this table carefully and try to see the pattern – see if you can extend it a little way.

Decimal count	Binary count	Hexadecimal
0	0	0
1	1	1
2	10	2
3	11	3
4	100	4
5	101	5
6	110	6
7	111	7
8	1000	8
9	1001	9
10	1010	A
11	1011	B
12	1100	C
13	1101	D
14	1110	E
15	1111	F
16	10000	10

Binary

To bring together the ideas of memory with those of the binary number system, simply imagine the switches having states on and off labelled by 1 and 0 respectively. Now, to represent the number 15, say, in the switch memory banks, you would need four switches, all of them in the on state – see the above table. The numbers 1 and 0 are called *binary digits*, or *bits* for short. We say, for instance, that the above table uses up to five bits maximum.

To reinforce the above, and to give you a method of converting binary into decimal, you can use the BIN function. Unfortunately, the BIN function can only act on a series of 1s and 0s, and you cannot, for instance, use INPUT to input a binary number into A$, and then use BIN VAL A$ to find the decimal equivalent. If you want to find the decimal equivalent of 1001011, for instance, simply key in:

    PRINT BIN 1001011

The computer will reply with: 75.

It is important to be able to represent numbers ranging from small to large in a computer, and as the above table illustrates, the actual size of the number determines how many bits are required to represent it. It is essential to be able to store and retrieve information in memory from compartments which can be addressed logically and easily. To this end, memory devices are usually split up into equal groups of bits, and in the Spectrum there are eight bits in each memory compartment.

This has very important implications for the electronics. Each compartment has its own electronic address, and the electronics can store and retrieve data at will, as explained in Chapter 1. For the moment, think of each compartment as being just like one of the rows of eight switches introduced above. Each 8-bit compartment can store one of 256 combinations of 1s and 0s. For instance, any number from 0 to 255 would fit in if converted to binary, but how would you store a number like 328 or 6.43 in binary? The answer to this question takes us off the central track of this book, but suffice it to say that if you line up several of these compartments, end to end, you can have as many bits as you like in a number. To represent decimal points is also a question of grouping the compartments correctly.

Binary and electronics

Binary is very important to a description of the electronics of the machine, as electronic lines in the computer system have 1s and 0s on them as +5 V and 0 V levels at any instant. Thus the state of a bus of lines (see Chapter 1) at any instant is best described by a binary number. The address bus, for instance, has 16 lines, thus any address can be represented by a 16-bit number. However, writing a 16-bit number down, and remembering it is rather difficult for humans to do without error. This leads us to look for a method of simplifying large binary numbers, and thus being able to write down and perhaps discuss the rather complex state of a large number of electronic lines in a simple form.

Hexadecimal and addresses

It is very convenient to split a large binary number into groups of four bits, and write down the patterns in a compact form. The Spectrum manual tells you how to do this, and we will look at an example of how addresses can be written in hexadecimal form. The table above shows you the hexadecimal label which may be applied to any group of four bits.

Chapter 1 shows you that the address, which the MPU is contacting at any time, appears as a binary state on the sixteen address bus lines. The address map of the Z80 starts at 0, i.e. all address lines at 0 V, and goes up to address 65,535. The binary for this is 1111 1111 1111 1111, and the hex for it is FFFF, using the above table. What would the half-way address be in this map? To see the answer, notice that there are 65536 address locations (0 to 65535). Half of this is 32768. The binary for this number is 1000 0000 0000 0000, and the hex is 8000. Notice that in order to talk of these 16-bit numbers, it is necessary to split them into smaller groups. See how much easier the hex code is for these quantities. But, why do we not simply stick to the fairly simple decimal representations? The answer is that for pure BASIC programming, this is perfectly acceptable, even preferable because we can easily manipulate our familiar decimal number system. However, if you wish to talk electronically, using the decimal number for the electronic state of a bus of lines is actually worse than using the pure binary. Imagine being told that the current bus state on the address bus should be 45741 in decimal, and you want to use a meter to check it. It would take you some time to work out that this meant:

A15 A14 A13 A12 A11 A10 A9 A8 A7 A6 A5 A4 A3 A2 A1 A0
 1   0   1   1   0   0 1 0 1 0 1 0 1 1 0 0

If, however, you were given it as B2AC, you would be able to generate the above binary state with ease, either using the table of hex to binary conversion, or after a very short time being able to do it automatically. It is more natural, in electronics, for the states of a given set of lines to be given in hex, as this is almost binary, and very easy to assimilate. Thus, the address map in Chapter 1 has hex addresses, as well as the decimal ones. For BASIC, of course, you will need decimal addresses, for functions such as PEEK, POKE, IN and OUT.

Converting between hex and decimal

The following is a program which converts between hex and decimal, and *vice versa*. If you are interested in the method of conversion, you will be able to take it from this – there is an explanation after the program. Alternatively, simply store the program, and call it up whenever you require the conversion.

```
10 INPUT "HEX or DEC input?
   (H or D)=",A$
```

```
 20 IF A$="H" THEN GOTO 1000
 30 IF A$<>"D" THEN GOTO 10
 40 REM Now convert DEC to HEX
 50 INPUT "Input whole no.<=65535",N
 60 IF N=65535 THEN LET H$="FFFF":
    GOTO 2000
 70 LET H$=""
 80 LET K=INT (N/4096)
 90 IF K<> 0 THEN GOSUB 500: LET H$=S$
100 LET L=N-K*4096
105 REM Now how many 256's
110 LET K=INT (L/256)
120 IF K=0 THEN IF H$<>""
    THEN LET H$=H$+STR$ 0
130 IF K<>0 THEN GO SUB 500: LET H$=H$+S$
140 LET L=L-K*256
150 REM Now for the 16's
160 LET K=INT (L/16)
170 IF K=0 THEN IF H$<>"" THEN
    LET H$=H$+STR$ 0
180 IF K<>0 THEN GO SUB 500: LET H$=H$+S$
190 LET L=L-K*16
200 IF L=0 THEN LET H$=H$+STR$ 0:GOTO 2000
210 LET K=L: GO SUB 500
220 LET H$=H$+S$
230 GOTO 2000
500 REM Routine to change DEC. digits
    into HEX.
510 IF K<=9 THEN LET S$=STR$K: RETURN
520 LET R$="ABCDEF"
530 LET T=K-9
540 LET S$=R$(T TO T)
550 RETURN
1000 REM Now for HEX to DEC conversion.
1010 INPUT "Input 4 or less HEX digits",A$
1020 LET K=0
1030 LET T=LEN A$
1040 FOR I=T TO 1 STEP -1
1050 LET K$=A$(I TO I)
1060 GOSUB 1500
1070 LET K=K+P*16 (T-I)
1080 NEXT I
1090 GO TO 3000
1500 REM Routine to convert a
     HEX digit to Decimal.
```

```
1510 IF K$>="0" THEN IF K$<="9" THEN
     LET P=VAL K$: RETURN
1520 LET P=(CODE K$)-55
1530 RETURN
2000 PRINT "The HEX ans. = ",H$
2010 GOTO 4000
3000 PRINT "The DEC ans. = ",K
4000 INPUT "Another no.? (Y or N)",A$
4010 IF A$="Y" THEN GO TO 10
4020 CLS : PRINT "Program ends."
```

To see how this program works, consider how hex numbers are formed. They are simply numbers counted according to base 16, just as we normally count to base 10. The numbers 0–F can be converted using the table in this appendix. Higher numbers are formed in a manner very similar to our decimal system, which is explained above. To count above F in the hex system, we must start a new column, just as counting above 9 in decimal requires a new column. Thus, the next number above F in hex is 10. Do not confuse this with the number ten, in decimal. Each time you reach a power of 16 (in hex) you start a new column. Thus:

$$1 \text{ (dec)} = 1 \text{ (hex)}$$
$$16 \text{ (dec)} = 10 \text{ (hex)}$$
$$256 \text{ (dec)} = 100 \text{ (hex)}$$
$$4096 \text{ (dec)} = 1000 \text{ (hex)}$$

This is as far as we need to go, as we do not need more than four hex digits in this book, but the system can, of course, be carried on as far as you like.

To convert a hex number into a decimal number, consider the following example:

$$A\,3\,5\,E = A \times 4096 = 3 \times 256 + 5 \times 16 + E$$
$$= 10 \times 4096 + 3 \times 256 + 5 \times 16 + 14 = 41{,}822 \text{ (in decimal)}$$

The right-hand digit – called the *least significant digit* or LSD – is the number of units in the number. The next digit to the left is the number of 16s, then comes the number of 256s, and finally the *most significant digit* or MSD – the number of 4096s. This shows the basis of the above program's conversion process for hex to decimal.

To convert the other way, the program finds out how many 4096s there are in the number (by division). This is the MSD, unless it is zero. Then, the remainder is divided by 256, and that gives the next digit. The remainder is again divided, this time by 16 for the next digit, and the final remainder is the LSD. This book uses numbers between 0 and FFFF in hex, or 0 and 65,535 in decimal. Note that this gives 65,536 numbers, as 0 is included.

The program also contains a method of converting between hex and decimal digits. You should try and see how it works.

You will be able to use hexadecimal almost as second nature after a little practice. Remember that it has been invented to make the electronics easier to deal with, and as you become proficient in its use, you will see why.

Binary to decimal and *vice versa*

To convert from binary to decimal, we will look at an example. Suppose we need to convert 10010111 to decimal. We could group in fours, convert to hex, and then convert to decimal. The alternative is to use the following type of table:

128	64	32	16	8	4	2	1
1	0	0	1	0	1	1	1

Where there is a 1, add in the number above it. The total is the number required. Here the number is: 128+16+4+2+1=151. To convert decimal into binary requires a division exactly as for decimal to hex. Suppose the number 4271 is to be converted into binary. The following shows the method:

$$
\begin{array}{lll}
4271 \ / \ 2 = & 2135 \text{ remainder } 1 & \text{LSB} \\
2135 \ / \ 2 = & 1067 \text{ remainder } 1 & \\
1067 \ / \ 2 = & 533 \text{ remainder } 1 & \\
533 \ / \ 2 = & 266 \text{ remainder } 1 & \\
266 \ / \ 2 = & 133 \text{ remainder } 0 & \\
133 \ / \ 2 = & 66 \text{ remainder } 1 & \\
66 \ / \ 2 = & 33 \text{ remainder } 0 & \\
33 \ / \ 2 = & 16 \text{ remainder } 1 & \\
16 \ / \ 2 = & 8 \text{ remainder } 0 & \\
8 \ / \ 2 = & 4 \text{ remainder } 0 & \\
4 \ / \ 2 = & 2 \text{ remainder } 0 & \\
2 \ / \ 2 = & 1 \text{ remainder } 0 & \\
1 \ / \ 2 = & 0 \text{ remainder } 1 & \text{MSB}
\end{array}
$$

(all further divisions give 0 remainder 0)

The binary number is composed of the remainders, with the last bit above as the most significant bit (MSB). Thus:

4271 = 1000010101111

This is a 13-bit representation of 4271. If you need a 16-bit representation, simply add leading zeros to form:

4271 = 0001 0000 1010 1111

Using the table, this equals the hex number: 106F.

The K and M notation

Your Spectrum will either be a 16K or a 48K version. This refers to the number of bytes of RAM storage available in the machine (see Chapter 1). As all addressing in the machine uses binary numbers, it is not natural to talk of units of one thousand bytes – this is a base-10 number. The nearest power of 2 to one thousand in binary is 2 to the 10th, or 1024 and this is the K unit in computers. Thus 16K means 16×1024, or 16384. Similarly, 48K=48×1024=49152. The largest memory location in the Spectrum is numbered 65,535. Thus, including the location numbered 0, there are

$$64 \times 1024 = 65536 = 64K \text{ bytes}$$

possible in the machine.

The K is still often called 'kilo', as if it were 1000, but you will have to convert this in your mind to 1024 if you require accuracy.

Megabytes is another term used in computing, and 1 Mbyte = 1048576 bytes. Again this is a power of 2. Two to 20th equals 1 Mega in computing. As you can see, when you are given 1 Mbyte of storage, you have nearly 48K more than you would have if you were given 1 million bytes.

Appendix Two
Electronics, Components, and Soldering

Introduction

Digital electronics, which includes most of computer engineering, is very much a question of plugging together standard integrated circuits, which perform high level functions for you. There is little actual electronics which you will need in this book, and any that come up is described as you need it. This appendix gives you some help in starting up an electronic project, the sort of tools you need, and such things as how to solder, and how to recognise different components.

Electricity and electronics

When the terminals of a battery are shorted together, a flow of sub-microscopic particles (electrons) flows from one terminal to the other. As this current flows, it can be made to do work, just as for water flow – in fact you should remember this similarity, and think of it when you come up against electrical devices. For instance, just as a narrow pipe will resist water flow, a current passed through a thin wire will be impeded, and a friction-like effect causes the wire to heat up. We say that the wire has a *resistance* to the flow. If the heat is intense enough, the wire glows, and can be used as a light or heater.

Current flow is usually attended by an increase in temperature somewhere, and the fact that your Spectrum becomes hot fairly quickly (especially the 48K version) is an indication that current is flowing through it. The Spectrum, of course, does not use a battery; it taps the mains electricity supply for its current. This current is doing work inside your Spectrum all the time, and the amount of work it performs per second is called *power*. That is what is meant when we say that the power of an electric barfire is, say, 1 kilowatt. It is a measure of the amount of work (or energy) being consumed per second, and hence the cost! In microelectronics, we try to keep the actual power to an absolute minimum, to allow us to use small power supplies, and generate as little heat as possible.

Current flow in a wire can only occur when there is a voltage between its ends, and this can be achieved in a number of ways. There is a voltage maintained between the terminals of a battery, for instance, by chemical means. There is voltage fed to our houses through the mains. This voltage is changing polarity all the time, and we call it AC (alternating current). Batteries give DC (direct current) and produce a very smooth voltage.

The ZX power supply gives a type of DC which is not smooth, but never swops its polarity around – it has a positive and a negative terminal like a battery, but its voltage ripples slightly, and changes in voltage as more or less current is taken from it. It is called an unregulated or 'raw' DC supply. It can be used to give smooth DC very easily, and this is what is done in the PSU section of the Spectrum (Fig. 1.2). An example of such a PSU is given in Chapter 2 for you to power the project described there and later.

In order to shuffle information around the buses of the computer, with the minimum of power, designers try to use low voltages, with very little current. The standard logic voltage is +5 V, and though there is very little current along each line, it is detectable, but generally disregarded. Thus, when we talk of electronic information being sent from one place to another, we mean that the voltage along some lines is changing.

The information is placed on bus lines by fast electronic switches, which act very much like water taps. They open and close to change the voltage on the line according to some set sequence, and the receiving device uses these voltages to switch its internal components on and off, and thus reacts to the incoming signal. In fact, the internal wiring of a computer is continually buzzing with changing voltages, millions of times a second. It is impossible to trap this information without fast electronic devices, which are synchronised to the processes.

To build the necessary hardware, a certain amount of familiarity with electronic construction is required, and this is described below.

Tools

The tools which you will require are simple, and fairly cheap. You will need a good pair of side cutters. These are used for cutting wire and component pins, and should be specially designed for the purpose. A large pair of heavy gauge wire cutters will not be acceptable. You will need a small and a large flat-head electrical screwdriver. A pair of pliers, again for small electrical work, will be useful, as well as a pair of wire strippers. You will also need a 15 W soldering iron with a medium to fine iron-clad bit, and some flux-cored electrical solder. Try to buy some fairly fine solder, as large diameter solder will encourage you to put too much solder onto the job. A 5X or 10X magnifying glass is essential to inspect your solder joints. Another important piece of equipment is a multimeter with a resistance scale. This is used to observe voltages, currents, and check on electrical continuity. You should read the instructions of this device, and practise measuring some resistances and battery voltages.

General components

The simplest electronic components are plugs, sockets, wire, switches, lights, resistors and capacitors, followed by diodes, transitors, and then integrated circuits. These components are described below. You should be able to buy them all from a component supplier, and there are many advertised in the electronic magazines – simply look on the shelves of any newsagent. You may have to buy parts mail order, though electronic component shops are springing up by the dozen, and there may be one near you – see Appendix 4.

To expand your Spectrum, you will need to purchase a socket to which you can solder a set of wires. It is worth buying this component immediately, and again look into the magazines, and phone around to find the correct one – simply mention that it is for the Spectrum. The actual socket required is a 0.1 in pitch double-28-way PCB edge connector, with solder bucket or wire-wrap pins, open ends, and a polarising key in position 5. See Appendix 3 for the pin-out. The wires soldered to this socket will connect to a board on which you will solder some components to perform various functions.

Any lights used in the projects will generally be LEDs (light emitting diodes), though higher current lights can also be controlled. The wiring for most of the work should be by thin plastic-insulated multi-strand or single-strand wire. Single-strand is useful for internal wiring on a board, while multi-strand is best for flying leads. Where a fairly complex board has to be constructed, the best wire to use is wire-wrap wire. This is a very thin insulated solid wire, and will make the wiring considerably neater. However, you will need some practice in its use before tackling a project. This is explained shortly.

The type of switches generally used throughout are subminiature toggle switches, and subminiature push-button switches. The exact switches used will not matter, but this is microelectronics, and it is as well to keep all the components neat and compact.

There are many systems of prototyping system for the Spectrum on the market, and many of them are excellent. If you wish to buy one of these, to aid you in wiring up the experiments described here you should try to see the ones you are interested in before buying. Some of them are over expensive, and not much better than simply using a standard strip-board, with copper tracks laid down on it which you can modify and personalise for yourself. Veroboard is a good example of such a strip-board, and this is the material which will be referred to throughout this book (see Fig. A.1). Component pins are pushed through from the insulated side to the copper tracks below and soldered in place. The holes are at a pitch of 0.1 in to accommodate a common pin-pitch.

Figure A.1 shows the most common electronic components, along with their circuit diagrammatic symbol.

Switches

The switch illustrated is a toggle switch, and as the toggle is changed over, switch contacts within the body of the device open and close. The diagram shows two common types of contact. The second of these is called a change-over, or single-pole double-throw switch, and has three pins. Switches can have several sets of contacts ganged together, and all actuated by the toggle, which may itself have several positions.

Resistors

Resistors are used for many purposes in electronics. In general, the resistors mentioned are the cheapest quarter-watt, 5% carbon resistors. Other types will do, but you should steer clear of 'wire-wound' resistors, as their electronic 'inductance' can interfere with the normal working of the computer.

The resistor illustrated shows the common method of labelling as to value. This is by a colour code. For the resistor type mentioned above, there will be a gold band on the body of the resistor to show which end is which, and to denote that this is a 5% tolerance component. The other bands give the actual value according to the following table.

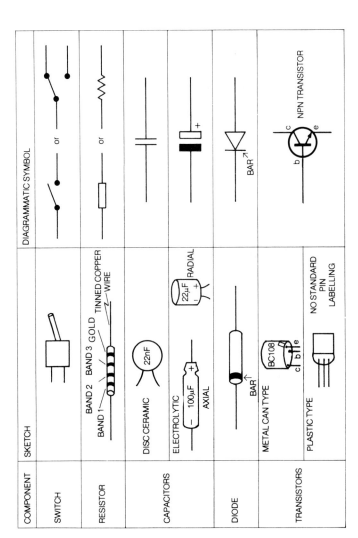

Fig. A.1. Components.

Band 1 or 2 colour	Value
Black	0
Brown	1
Red	2
Orange	3
Yellow	4
Green	5
Blue	6
Purple	7
Grey	8
White	9

These values give the number of zeros after the value if they appear in band 3. Note that black in band three means 'zero zeros' – i.e. it denotes no colour.

Values of resistors are measured in units of ohms – the higher the value the more resistant to current flow. Ohms is often denoted by a Greek 'omega' (Ω). To simplify the classification, thousands of ohms is denoted by a K and millions by an M. Fractions of a K are often written as 2K7 instead of 2.7K because otherwise the decimal point may be missed. Similarly 4M7 for megohms. Ohms itself is often denoted by an R. Thus 100 ohms is often written 100R. These are the conventions used in this book.

Examples of use of the colour code are:

Band 1	Band 2	Band 3	Value	
Brown	Red	Black	1 2 –	= 12 ohms or 12R
Brown	Red	Brown	1 2 0	= 120R
Yellow	Purple	Red	4 7 00	= 4K7
Brown	Black	Yellow	1 0 0000	= 100K
Brown	Black	Orange	1 0 000	= 10K
Yellow	Purple	Green	4 7 00000	= 4M7

You can gain some practice with your multimeter by checking the resistances of some of these components using the resistance ranges.

Capacitors

Capacitors are used to store electronic energy. They can smooth ripples in a power supply, and they can block out DC signals. Their main use in this book is for smoothing. When they are referred to, the type of component required will be stated to ensure that you use the right one.

Capacitors are marked on their surface. They are measured in units of *farads*. However, this unit is far too large for normal use, and the largest values you will probably meet will be in microfarads, or millionths of a farad. The next lower unit is nanofarads, or 1000th of a microfarad, and then comes 1000 times less again with picofarads. These are written μF, nF and pF respectively. The Greek letter mu (μ) is pronounced 'micro' here. The voltage up to which the component may be used is important for electrolytics, and this is normally stated on the can of the component. The diagram shows two styles of electrolytic. It is also important to connect electrolytics the correct way round.

If you try to find the resistance of one of these devices, you should find that it is infinite. A capacitor will not pass a DC current, but it will pass an AC current.

Diodes

Diodes have the characteristic of conducting electric current in just one direction. This is useful in preventing certain types of data from travelling from one place to another, as is seen in the book, and for turning AC into DC. The diode was the first type of semiconductor discovered, and is the precursor to transistors and everything we have today in modern electronics. The diagrammatic symbol for the diode is shown, along with a means of determining which way round it fits – the bar on the body of the device ties up with the bar end in the diagram. Figure A.2 shows a diagrammatic example of how a diode acts. When the battery is connected across it with the negative electrode to the bar, the diode switches on and conducts current from one side of the battery to the other. When the battery is reversed, no flow occurs. Diodes have the further useful characteristic of maintaining an almost constant voltage drop across themselves when switched on. Thus, no matter what current flows through a diode the voltage across the diode is the same. This constant voltage is called the 'forward voltage', and if the power supply voltage fed to the diode is not above this forward voltage, the diode remains off.

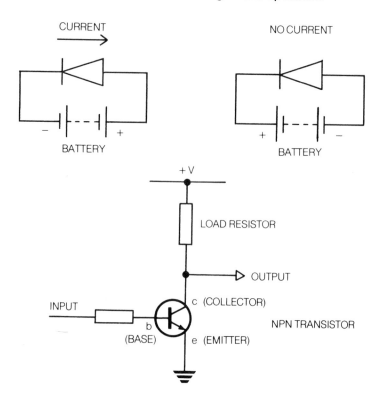

Fig. A.2. Diodes and transitors.

Again, your meter can be used to check the diode. You will see a low resistance in one direction, and a high resistance in the other. Some diodes, however, have a forward voltage which is too high for the low voltage battery in the multimeter, and you will then see a high resistance in both directions as the diode does not switch on. Some of the more expensive meters have a higher voltage battery internally for their resistance ranges, for this exact reason. The LED mentioned later will not switch on without this higher voltage battery.

Transistors

There are many different types of transistor, and two styles of package are illustrated in Fig. A.1. A transistor has three pins or wires, the *collector* (c), the *base* (b) and *emitter* (e), as shown. The type of transistor illustrated is an NPN device – this means that the collector has to be positive with respect to the emitter for the device to work. In digital electronics, a transistor is used simply as a switch, and if a signal is applied to the base it will switch the transistor on or off. The circuit shown in Fig. A.2 includes two resistors, and is a common circuit used throughout the book. The emitter is connected to the ground, or 0 V, and when the input is also at 0, the transistor is off, and the output is pulled up to the power supply voltage (+V) by the load resistor. The output is thus at a 1 – the opposite to the input. When the input is taken positive, the transistor switches on, and connects the output to ground. It is therefore at 0, again opposite to the input. If the load resistor is a very low resistance, the transistor is hard put to fight this, and the output may not reach near enough to 0 V. On the other hand, if the load is a high resistance, the output may not be properly pulled up to +V. A balance must be struck. Also, notice how the transistor does not conduct any current through the load when it is off, but does do when it is on. This can be used to control the current in a relay, for instance, as in Chapter 2.

Transistor theory is complex, and beyond the scope of this book, but the sketch above will help you to follow transistor use in the book. They are used for a number of applications, but their main use is as an amplifier. Only a very small signal is needed at the input to switch the transistor on, and change the output from +V to 0 V. The input resistor is often needed to limit the current taken from the input signal.

You can connect your multimeter in series with the load resistor, and select a high DC current reading. You will see a current flow when the transistor is switched on.

Integrated circuits

Figure A.1 shows a typical integrated circuit (IC) or 'chip'. This is called a DIL or dual in line package, and has a number of pins along the two sides. The diagram shows you how to tell the orientation of the IC, and how the numbering of the pins goes. This is the same for all the ICs in this book, which range from 16-pin to 40-pin chips. In general, you are advised to use special DIL IC sockets for these components to fit into, thus saving having to solder the actual ICs to the board. Sockets allow you to change faulty ICs, and even remove them for re-use.

Always take care when inserting ICs into their sockets, as it is easy to bend a pin beneath the body of the IC, or leave a pin sticking out over the side of the socket. This is a common cause of faulty circuitry, and you should check this as a first step to finding any malfunction. You may find it easier to bend the two rows of IC pins further in together, as they are always supplied a little splayed out – this helps to retain them when inserted into printed circuit boards, but makes them more difficult to insert into a socket.

To remove an IC body and the socket, a small screwdriver should be inserted between the IC body and the socket. The IC should be levered up slowly and with the minimum of force, until its pins are clear of the socket holes.

It is always a good idea to check the power supply before inserting an IC into its socket. This should be done by using the voltage range of your multimeter, and connecting to the actual socket itself. You should particularly check that the voltage is the correct way round.

Strip-board

One of the most common methods of contstructing prototype circuitry is to use an insulating board, with copper strips running along its length. One of the most common types of this material is Veroboard. This is an insulating material with a 0.1 in matrix of holes, and copper strips adhering to the underside of the board. The holes go through the copper strips, and allow you to push the pins and wires of components through from the top of the board, to be soldered underneath. This is an excellent method of fixing the components in place, and the copper strips can be used to form some of the connections of the circuit. Veroboard is illustrated in Fig. A.1.

The use of Veroboard is described in the projects of this book, and a later section suggests some simple construction practice you can try if you have no experience of soldering or electronic construction.

LEDs and relays

The light emitting diode has the same properties as the diodes mentioned above, except that it emits light when switched on. Figure A.3 shows the symbol and actual form of the LED. You can use a small battery to check on its polarity using the circuit shown in Fig. A.3. You will do it no damage by applying the voltage the wrong way round, but you must always use a resistor of the sort of value shown in series with the LED, or it will draw excess current and be damaged. The voltage shown should not be increased too far without increasing the resister value. You can use your multimeter on the milliamps range to check on the current flowing. It should not exceed about 15 mA.

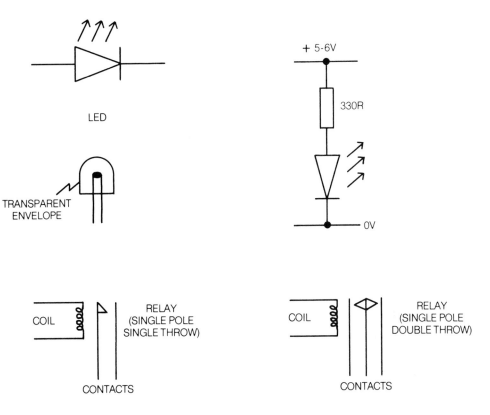

Fig. A.3. LEDs and relays.

The LED is confined to a transparent envelope as shown, and there are several colours now available.

Relays are explained in Chapter 2, and Fig. A.3 shows two diagrammatic symbols for this component. One version shows a coil of wire, and a couple of switch contacts; the other shows the same but with a changeover switch. One side will be normally open, and the other side normally closed. When a current is allowed to flow in the coil, the relay contacts change state, and can be used to control another electrical device.

Construction and soldering

To practise constructing electronic devices, you will need some Veroboard, and a few components such as resistors, capacitors and a couple of IC sockets. You should also buy all three types of wire recommended above.

First, gain some familiarity with the side cutters. Cut off a few inches of wire of different types, and try to strip the insulation without cutting the wire itself. This is particularly difficult for the wire-wrap wire. It is not easy to pair the insulation off without breaking the wire inside. Try closing the jaws of the side cutters gently on the insulation, and pulling it off. You will eventually be able to do this without breaking the wire inside. There are special wire strippers which you can buy for this purpose – they draw a set of adjustable sprung jaws across the insulation, and adjust themselves to the shape of the wire as they go. These are very successful, but expensive. You can also buy a special wire-wrap stripping tool, and this is cheaper and very good for the purpose.

The larger diameter wire should be easier for you to strip, and for short lengths you should hold the piece in the pliers, dig the side cutter jaws into the wire insulation a couple of millimetres from the end, and pull the insulation off. This also takes a certain amount of practice, and you have to learn to 'feel' how far to dig the side cutter jaws into the insulation without cutting the wire.

The next step is to learn how to make solder joints. In this section we shall practise soldering components onto Veroboard. However, the first step is to learn to use the soldering iron.

If this is the first time that your soldering iron has been switched on, you should be careful to apply some solder to the tip as it warms up. This is called 'tinning' the bit, and the flux in the solder will help the solder flow onto the tip and protect it from becoming oxidised. When up to temperature, try tinning some of the Veroboard. Lay the board on a level surface with the copper strips showing, and touch the copper with the soldering iron. You should then immediately apply a little solder to the joint between the copper and the soldering iron, and try to allow the molten solder to flow along the copper. It is difficult to start the flow, as Veroboard is coated to stop it oxidising, but once through this surface layer, the solder will flow fairly freely along the board. Do not leave the soldering iron in one place for too long, or the board will be damaged. This is a general rule for all components, and you should practise making solder joints in the shortest possible time. Keep on practising tinning Veroboard until you can apply a smooth and even layer of solder onto the surface, with no blobs. From time to time you will have to clean the soldering iron tip. This should be done by quickly wiping across a piece of wet sponge. When the iron itself has a large blob of solder on the tip, you should shake it off onto some paper to prevent a blob of solder being left on the work.

The next step is to tin some of the wire, and component pins and wires. Always tin the iron just before doing any soldering, to ensure that the solder is flowing properly. Check that the wire to be tinned is clean, and bring tip and solder into contact with the wire as shown in Fig. A.4. This should leave a layer of bright solder on the wire, and once again try not to leave a large blob of solder, but rather a thin and

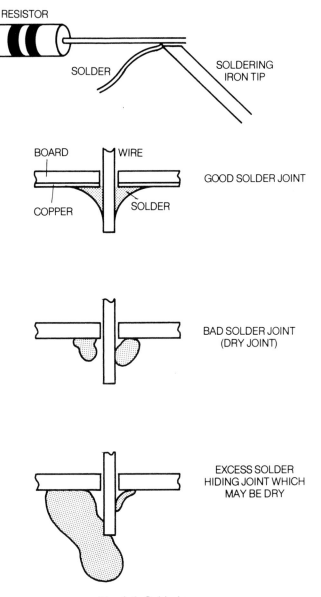

Fig. A.4. Soldering.

complete layer on the surface. This is worth practising until you are confident, and can tin the wire quickly to prevent too much heat from reaching the component.

To prepare a piece of stranded wire for soldering to a piece of work, the wire should be stripped, and the strands twisted together to help prevent the odd strand from sticking out during soldering. The wire should then be tinned as above, ensuring that solder flows right into the strands of wire, binding them together fully.

The tinning process should always be the first step to performing any soldering. If the iron has been left unused for more than 20 seconds or so, it should also be tinned. When you tin it, smoke will be produced to show you that flux is being burned off the tip. When the smoke ceases, there is no flux left, and tinning is necessary.

The tinned wire should then be pushed through one of the holes on a piece of Veroboard, and the board turned over to show the copper strip with the wire poking through. This can be soldered in place as follows. Always push components in from the insulated side of the board, to the copper strips below. You should do the same with connecting wires – it will be much easier to check, and form a more robust construction if all your wiring appears above the board, and is soldered below.

The Veroboard cannot be tinned before the joint is made, as this often blocks up the hole. It should not be necessary, as tinning can be done as the joint is made. However, a certain amount of care is necessary. Tin the iron tip as usual, and bring it up to contact both the wire and the copper strip on the board. Run a small amount of solder into the joint, and this will help to allow heat to travel from the iron to the joint. If you run the solder in just right, you will produce a joint similar to the 'good solder joint' in Fig. A.4. If the solder does not flow properly, the dry joint shown will be formed as the solder turns into a ball as shown, or does not properly 'weld' or 'flow' to the copper and wire. If too much solder is used, the third type of joint is produced. A dry joint may appear to have physically joined the wire to the copper, but this will in fact be due to a hard layer of insulating flux, and not a metallic joint. The key to soldering is watching the solder flow onto the surfaces to be joined. You should practise this until you can produce good neat joints with a nice clean look to them, as shown in Fig. A.4.

A difficult type of joint to make is the type where the wire pushed through the hole is very much smaller than the hole itself. This is the case with wire-wrap wire, and you should practise this until you can ensure good results. Try bending the wire over after insertion to retain it in the hole. Be careful to trim excess wire off, being careful not to shatter the solder joint. Never leave a piece of uninsulated wire around which might be able to short across the tracks. You should strip the minimum of insulation off the wire at all times.

The next component to practise on is the IC socket. You will find that Veroboard has the correct pitch of holes for ICs. To fix one of these to the board, push the pins through the holes in the board, and bend two corner pins over to retain the socket. Always insert IC sockets in so that the copper strips run across the IC. Cut the tracks connecting one side of the socket to the other beneath the board.

With the IC socket retained in the board, it can be turned over. Solder just two pins of the socket, at opposite corners, and then hold the board and socket so that the socket it pressed against the board, and touch the two solder joints with the iron. If the socket is not properly against the board, it will click down into place, and the solder will harden with the socket and board fully in contact. The rest of the joints can now be made, joining the IC socket pins to the copper tracks. The joints themselves must be made with the greatest of care to run just enough solder in, and no more. The pins are very near to each other, and it is easy to leave a solder bridge or minute solder flash between nearby tracks. Each solder joint must be checked thoroughly with a magnifying glass, and if you cannot see a clear line of insulation between tracks, apply the soldering iron again until you are sure. Inspection is made a lot easier if you wipe the joints clean of flux using a little methylated spirit.

You should practise the techniques above until you are sure you can make good solder joints, with no shorts, and without using excess heat which could damage your components.

Appendix Three

The Spectrum Edge Connector

Figure A.5 shows a view of the edge connector from the back of the Spectrum, and corrects the one in the Spectrum manual which is viewed from a strange angle. Make sure that you purchase the correct edge-socket, and always use a polarising tab in the slot of the socket as this will locate the connector correctly. Without this polarising tab it is most awkward to insert the connector in the right position, and inspection of the positioning is not easy.

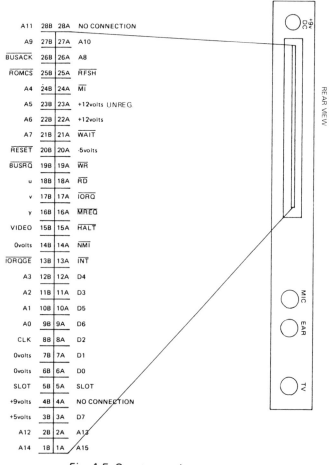

Fig. A.5. Spectrum edge connector.

Appendix Four
Sources of Components and Devices

Throughout the book components are given names and labels which should make them easy to find. The following list of suppliers will help in buying all that you need.

Technomatic Ltd.,
17 Burnley Rd.,
London, NW10 1ED
Phone: 01-452 1500 or 01-450 6597

Technomatic are general electronic component suppliers. They have a very large stock, and can supply to mail order or over the counter at any of their shops. The stepper motor recommended in Chapter 4 is available through Technomatic.

RS Components Ltd.,
PO Box 99,
Corby,
Northants, NN17 9RS
Phone: 0536-201234

RS have a wide stock of components, and a standard catalogue which is worth obtaining. They also publish comprehensive data sheets on many electronic products, and these will be of great value. The standard RS number is given in the text for some of the items required, and these can be used as a basis for describing the required component in general.

Powertran Cybernetics Ltd.,
Portway Industrial Estate,
Andover,
Hants, SP10 3NN
Phone: Andover 0264-64455

Powertran manufacture the Micro Grasp robot described in Chapter 5.

They also manufacture a family of larger hydraulically powered robots called the Genesis series which are suitable for industrial use.

Colne Robotics Co. Ltd.,
Beaufort Rd.,
East Twickenham,
Middx, TW1 2PQ
Phone: 01-892 8197

Colne supply the Armdroid described in Chapter 5. They supply other more sophisticated and larger robots too, along with a number of robotically controlled machine tools. They also sell a vision system called Colvis, which views the world using a solid state camera, and has some simple recognition functions.

Cyber Robotics Ltd.,
61 Ditton Walk,
Cambridge, CB5 8QD
Phone: 0223-210675

The Cyber 310 described in Chapter 5 is available through Cyber Robotics Ltd. Their robot arm is all ready to interface to an Acorn machine, but they have a Spectrum interface in development. No robot should be bought unless you are sure of the interfacing requirements, and details should be requested from Cyber if you are interested in the machine.

Glossary

AC: Alternating current. This describes an electrical current, or voltage, which continuously oscillates, and changes its polarity, rather than remaining constant as for a DC current or voltage. A voltage which changes, but does not actually change polarity, is said to 'ripple' rather than being AC.

Active low: A signal line is active low if it takes its active state when at 0 level. An example of this might be the enable line to an interface or memory block. To activate such a device, its enable line would have to be brought to ground level.

ADC: Analogue to digital converter. A device which converts continuously changing voltages to binary numbers for input to a computer. A continuously changing, or analogue, voltage is one which does not take on set levels of voltage values, but may take on any value within a range.

Address bus: A group of electronic lines which communicate memory addresses as binary patterns. The addresses are output by the MPU, and collected by devices connected to the address bus. A block of logic called the address decoding is responsible for recognising the addresses, and enabling the appropriate block.

Address decoding: A block of logic which monitors the address bus, and sets the enable line of a given device within the computer system to its active state when its address appears on the address bus. This block of logic decides the memory and I/O maps of the system.

Analogue: A signal which is capable of taking on continuously variable values is said to be an analogue variable. For instance, a temperature sensor would give out a voltage which is proportional to the temperature. The voltage values for different temperatures would be able to take on any value, and would not be restricted to having to take on set levels of voltage. This is as opposed to *digital*.

ASCII: American Standard Code for Information Interchange. This is a numerical coding for the set of letters, numbers and general symbols. An ASCII code is normally a single number between 0 and 127, and hence would be represented by a 7-bit number. However, this is normally extended to fill a complete byte, and thus most machines will allow up to 256 different characters, each of which is coded by a unique ASCII code number.

Binary: Expressed in a form which uses two levels, 1 and 0. A binary number is one which is formed entirely from 1s and 0s.

Bit: Binary digit. 1 and 0 are the binary digits. The 1s and 0s of a binary number are called *bits*.

Bus: Collection of electronic lines which are grouped together by virtue of having similar functions. See *address, data* and *control bus*.

Byte: 8 bits form a byte, and 8-bit microprocessors, such as the Z80, arrange their memory locations to contain bytes. A byte can contain a complete ASCII code, and hence may hold a single character. For floating point arithmetic, however, more than one byte is used to represent a general number, to obtain more accuracy.

Capacitor: Electronic component which stores electronic charge, and will not allow DC to pass through it. Capacitors are often used for smoothing the outputs of power supplies. There are two types of capacitor in this book: the electrolytic, and the disk ceramic. The electrolytic capacitor is capable of holding more charge than a ceramic, but must be connected into the circuit the correct way round. Disk ceramics are small value capacitors, and are used to remove high frequency noise on power supplies. Both types of capacitor are also used to block the passage of DC voltages.

Chip: Short form for the words silicon chip, or integrated circuit. Many transistors, resistors and capacitors may be formed on a chip, and these are interconnected on the chip by minute electronic pathways. The components and the pathways are all produced by an advanced form of photography.

Clock: An oscillator which serves to supply the timing for a computer's functioning. Each 'tick' of such a clock causes the MPU to enter a new part of its cycle. The frequency of the MPU clock thus determines the speed with which it processes a program. There is always a maximum frequency which an MPU or any other device can accept for its clock.

Control bus: Collection of electronic lines performing general control functions which allow the MPU to control the system electronically. Examples of lines within the control bus would be RD, WR, IORQ and MREQ. Other lines might include the reset line to the MPU. This bus is a little difficult to define fully, as not all the MPU control lines will always appear in the bus. It depends upon the design of the computer system itself. In addition, some extra non-MPU lines may be found useful in the control bus.

Control register: An internal memory location of an electronic device through which the microprocessor writes commands to the device. For instance, when using a PIO, its functions are fully controlled by the bits of its control registers. In order to set a line on its output high, the corresponding data register bit is set to 1. This is a general method of communicating with LSI I/O devices.

CPU: Central processing unit. The CPU of a computer is the arithmetic and logic centre of the machine. In addition, it is responsible for the electronic control of the system. In large computers, the CPU often spans a number of PCBs of electronic components. In a microcomputer, this is all confined to a single chip – the MPU. Thus, you may regard the word CPU, in microcomputing, as another name for the MPU.

Databus: Collection of lines which communicates a byte of data to or from the MPU. When the contents of a memory or I/O location are required by the MPU, it will first use the address bus to contact the correct device, and location within that device. The data from the location is then placed on the data bus by the device, and collected by the MPU. The process is reversed when the MPU wishes to write data out to the location.

Data register: An internal register of a device which may be accessed by the MPU to communicate data to and from the device. This normally applies to an I/O chip. The pattern of 1s and 0s on the output of an LSI parallel I/O chip would be changed by the MPU by its writing the required pattern to the chip's internal data register.

DC: Direct Current. This describes the output of a power source whose voltage does not oscillate – as opposed to *AC*. A battery is a very common source of DC.

Decimal: Our normal numbering system is based on the number 10, and hence the numbers are called decimal numbers. The system is also sometimes referred to as the denary system.

Digital: Relying upon separate levels rather than continuously variable levels, as opposed to *analogue*. Any variation which has set levels of value is said to be *digital*. For instance, a stepper motor is a digital device as its shaft can only turn by set defined amounts with each step. It cannot take on angular positions in between these angles.

Diode: An electronic component which blocks current flow in one direction. There are many types of diode, and many different uses for them. This book shows their use for rectifying AC to produce DC, as a method of protecting transistors from voltage spikes, as a means of blocking DC current in a given direction, and as small lights (LEDs).

Enable: An electronic line which is used to switch a device on or off. Memory devices have enable lines, and their data outputs are normally switched off until this enable goes to its active state. This is commonly caused by taking the enable to a low level.

Feedback: The activity of using a parameter which varies as some process occurs, and which may be used to monitor that process. An example is feedback of position for the movement of a lever under computer control. It is normal to gain feedback from a process by attaching sensors to the system, and monitoring a voltage fed back from the sensor.

Flowchart: A set of visual boxes which indicate the logical flow of a computer program without having to understand the computer programming language.

Heatsink: A sheet of metal, often aluminium, which is bolted to an electronic circuit to assist in the removal of heat.

Home sensor: A switch which is fixed to the movable part of a machine which closes when that part takes up a given home position. This is used as feedback to the computer to show that the home position has been reached.

Integrated circuit: A small package within which is a complete electronic circuit formed on a silicon chip. Integration is the process of taking an electronic circuit and producing it on a chip, rather than building it using discrete components such as transistors and resistors.

I/O: Input/Output. This refers to those electronic devices in a computer system which communicate with the outside world. This would include such devices as the buzzer, MIC and EAR sockets on the back of the Spectrum.

I/O map: The addresses within a computer system where the I/O devices are found.

LAS: Light-activated switch. This device closes a switch, or gives a digital output when incident light level exceeds a certain value.

LDR: Light-dependent resistor. This device changes its resistance according to the incident light level. A common form of LDR is the cadmium sulphide cell, or CDS cell. The resistance of the cell reduces with greater incident light levels, as the light particles (photons) activate more electrons on the surface of the device, for carrying an electric current.

LSI: Large scale integration. This refers to devices which contain large densities of components integrated onto a chip. The MPU is an LSI device, as is the PIO. The next classification below LSI is MSI, or medium scale integration, and below that is SSI, or small scale integration.

Machine code: The actual language of the MPU itself. The instructions are stored as binary numbers which are interpreted by the MPU directly. The MPU never executes BASIC directly. The computer always has to contain a program to control the keyboard and screen, and to translate the BASIC statements input to the computer into machine code. The Spectrum contains a program called an 'interpreter' for this purpose. This allows the MPU to be fed machine code, while the user communicates in BASIC.

Memory: Electronic devices which hold MPU instructions and data. There are two types of memory referred to in this book, both of them are formed on chips – they are RAM and ROM. These devices are sometimes referred to as semiconductor memory to distinguish them from cassette or disk storage.

Memory map: The set of addresses which memory devices take up in the computer system. The way in which the memory devices are arranged in the memory structure of the machine is determined by the address decoding logic.

Multi-meter: An electrical instrument for measuring voltages, currents and resistances.

Microcomputer: A computer system based around an MPU. The minimum required support chips for the MPU would include memory and I/O chips. It is possible to find chips which are complete microcomputers in their own right. These contain MPU, buses, memory and I/O on the same chip.

Microswitch: A sensitive electrical switch which can be switched by a small amount of force or movement.

Motor: An electrical machine which uses electromagnetism to rotate a shaft.

MPU: Microprocessing unit. This integrated circuit is at the heart of a microcomputer. It is able to scan through memory, execute instructions, and control the entire system via the system buses. See also *CPU.*

Parallel: Communication over a number of electronic lines simultaneously. The output lines of a PIO are parallel lines.

PCB: Printed circuit board. Used to hold and interconnect a number of electronic devices. The interconnections are by tracks of copper adhering to an insulating board normally made of fibre-glass or SRBP (a type of laminated paper). The copper is often coated with solder to help with soldering. The Spectrum uses a PTH (plated through hole) PCB. This connects tracks from top to bottom by holes coated internally with copper and solder.

Phoneme: The audible component of a spoken word. Any word may be analysed into its phoneme components, and the sound of any word may be produced by concatenating its phonemes.

PIO: Parallel I/O chip. This is an integrated circuit in the Z80 family of devices which allows up to 16 parallel I/O lines to be added to a computer. The MPU communicates with it by some internal PIO registers.

Potentiometer: Variable resistor. This is sometimes referred to as a 'pot' for short.

PSU: Power supply unit.

RAM: Random access memory. This type of memory chip holds information which may be written to, or read from, and which is usually volatile, i.e. the data disappears when power is removed from the system.

Real time clock: A clock which holds the time of day.

Regulator: Normally a voltage regulator which is used in a PSU to smooth its output voltage for supplying integrated circuits.

Relay: An electromechanical switch whose contacts are closed by applying a current to its internal coil.

Reset: A pin on an MPU which forces it to start from a known state, particularly when first switched on.

Resistor: An electronic component which reduces current flow.

Robot: A mechanical device which has automatic functions often controlled by feedback, and often having some form of learning response. Any mechanical device which is connected to be controlled by a computer could be called a robot, and the definition is not fully agreed.

ROM: Read only memory. This type of memory chip contains memory which cannot be changed. It is particularly useful for holding programs which control the computer, and must be available as soon as switched on.

Sensor: An electronic device for measuring and communicating the state of a physical variable to a computer system.

Servomotor: A type of motor which uses a positional or rotational sensor to feed back to a control system in order to monitor and hence control the motor's movement.

Solenoid: A coil of wire often formed around a magnetic core which is used to create a magnetic field when a current is passed through it.

SPC: Speech processing chip. This is used to turn previously stored speech data into recognisable human speech.

Speech recognition: This is the embryonic study of the computer recognition of human languages. It is the opposite of speech synthesis.

Speech synthesis: The electronic synthesis of spoken words. The words to be spoken can be communicated to some systems in the form of an ASCII string. It is more common, however, for a speech synthesis device to have a number of words stored in a ROM, and called up in a random manner for any given required utterance.

Stepper controller: An electronic device which converts the output of a computer into electrical control signals for a stepper motor.

Stepper motor: A motor whose shaft can be made to rotate through any number of equal angular steps. The motor does not spin continuously when connected to a power supply. A special controller is required. By gearing the shaft to a mechanical device, the device's movement can be controlled accurately.

Stripboard: A type of PCB which comes with copper strips and holes for inserting electronic components and building up general circuits from scratch.

Transformer: An electrical device which is used to step down or up the voltage of an AC power source.

ULA: Uncommitted logic array. This is a chip which may be defined before manufacture to contain a given electronic circuit. When a company has a large number of chips connected together to form a circuit, they can have the entire circuit integrated onto a customised ULA. The ULA in the Spectrum performs many control functions for the MPU, to save it from having to control them itself.

Video: This applies to the part of the computer which displays information on the screen.

Z80A: The industrial code name for the particular MPU used in the Spectrum.

Index